Creative Control
of Building Costs

THE AMERICAN INSTITUTE OF ARCHITECTS

EDITED BY

William Dudley Hunt, Jr., AIA
For The American Institute of Architects

Creative Control
of Building Costs

New York

San Francisco

M c G R A W - H I L L   B O O K   C O M P A N Y   Toronto

London

Sydney

CREATIVE CONTROL OF BUILDING COSTS

1234567890MP72106987

Preface

This book is unique. All the other books about the costs of constructing buildings have been concerned with the estimation of costs or with some other tool or process of cost control. This book takes as its premises that cost control is an intrinsic part of the creative design and construction process, that costs can be *controlled* not just *estimated*, and that cost control, as an integral part of the design process, can actively contribute to the creative process that produces good buildings.

Starting with a discussion of the overall theory of creative cost control, the chapters following discuss and demonstrate the principles upon which cost systems can be built, the legal and ethical implications of cost control, and the systems, methods, and techniques to be used. Cost control in every phase of architectural services is discussed, starting with the budget and continuing through to the completion of construction and even throughout the life of the building.

While it begins with a cost philosophy and develops a theory, the book is also very practical—the authors demonstrating the *how* of cost control along with the *why*.

The book was developed and written for The American Institute of Architects, its preparation and editing paid for out of funds from the Institute's supplemental dues program. It is a tangible example of the deep interest of the architectural profession, and of its professional organization, in the all-important area of control of building costs, both for the ultimate benefit of building owners and as an important aspect of building design and of architectural services.

Intended primarily for the use of architects and of the engineers, draftsmen, and others who work most closely with architects, the book

v

should also be of considerable value to financiers, building owners and developers, contractors, real estate brokers, and all of the others who participate in some way in the building construction industry.

At this juncture, it should be noted that the chapters of this book have been written by architects and other authorities, all of whom have a deep interest in cost control as an important part of the creative process of design and construction. A word or two is certainly in order about each of these authors who have given of their time and talent to produce the book.

The architects include William Dudley Hunt, Jr., AIA, Publisher of *AIA Journal,* who originated the concept of the book and directed its preparation and editing; Charles Luckman, FAIA, President of Charles Luckman Associates of Los Angeles and New York; George E. Kassabaum, FAIA, principal of Hellmuth, Obata and Kassabaum, Inc. of St. Louis and current Vice-president of the Institute; John R. Diehl, AIA, principal of Diehl and Stein of Princeton; Rolf Sklarek, AIA, Vice-president of Victor Gruen Associates with offices in Los Angeles, New York and other cities; and Bernard J. Grad, FAIA, principal of Frank Grad & Sons of Newark.

Other cost authorities who wrote chapters include: King Royer and Brad Howes, both professional engineers and Assistant Professors in the Department of Building Construction, University of Florida, Gainesville; Justin Sweet, Professor of Law, University of California, Berkeley; Gerald McKee, Jr., President of McKee-Berger-Mansueto, Inc., Construction Consultants, New York; Allen E. Cox, professional engineer, President of the Read-Cox Corporation, Consulting Engineers, Worcester, Mass.; James J. O'Brien, professional engineer, principal of Meridian Engineering of Philadelphia; Bohdan O. Szuprowicz, professional engineer, information management consultant and Senior Consultant, Diebold Group, Inc.; J. T. Greenberg, professional engineer, Manager of Construction Cost Control, Smith, Hinchman & Grylls Associates, Inc., Detroit; Irvin L. Timlin, Chief Estimator, Deeter-Richey-Sippel, Pittsburgh; Norman Foster, construction estimator with more than thirty years experience, General Manager, Robert Miller Construction Inc., Lockport, N.Y.

These authors have produced a book which should be part of the library of every person involved in the processes that produce buildings. Better than that, perhaps the book should be on their drafting tables and desks rather than on the shelves of their libraries.

CHARLES M. NES, JR., FAIA
President, The American Institute of Architects
May 15, 1967

Contents

Part Five   MAINTAINING CONTROL UNTIL BUILDING COMPLETION

Creative Control
of Building Costs

THE AMERICAN INSTITUTE OF ARCHITECTS

PART ONE

*Creative
Cost Control
for Buildings*

ONE

William Dudley Hunt Jr., AIA

Creative
Cost Control
for Buildings

A confirmed cynic once described architects—and those who work with them—as educated, cultured, respected, creative, professional, often capable of designing beautiful buildings that satisfy themselves but not their clients, buildings that fail to function properly and are always too expensive.

As in most cynicism, the case is vastly overstated; yet there is enough truth in the statement, particularly regarding costs, that it cannot be passed off as only unusually harsh criticism or bad manners.

When the man in the street is asked what he knows about architects and their services, too often he knows little enough other than the name of Frank Lloyd Wright and that he thinks architects cause buildings to cost more than they should. As if this were not bad enough, owners of buildings, when asked about the architectural services they received, concur too often with the widespread notion among less enlightened members of the public that architects *cause* buildings to cost more—and that, at best, the only return for the extra costs will be, possibly, better-looking buildings.

3

It should be quickly added, above the howls of indignation of those who do keep the costs of their buildings in line, that their successes, though very real, are certainly unsung among their publics and their clients. The sagas that spread across the country and seem to come down from generation to generation are those heralding the times when buildings come in half again above the budget, not the times when buildings are right on the money.

From this, it would seem obvious that architects, and all those who work with them, need a better press, need to better inform their publics and their clients. On the other hand, it should also be obvious, in a time when all architects are visited with the sins of a few, that there exist possibilities not only for better dissemination of information about architects' handling of the costs of construction, but also a need for better cost performance by architects.

It is a fact that there are architectural offices whose performance in the area of costs is very good indeed, offices with long records of success and well-deserved reputations for design within their clients' budgets. And there are others whose records are not so good. It should be added that even the offices whose cost performances are high are not without their problems in this area, are not without the need for new and improved methods of handling the costs of constructions.

There are those offices with highly developed systems of estimating costs, those that use Critical Path Method (CPM) scheduling and cost systems, those that have developed quantities of information about costs, those that habitually employ quantity surveying or similar methods for accurate takeoffs. There are even a few offices with sophisticated, complete systems of cost control, but these are in the minority. In many offices, cost control is a sometime thing. In some offices, it starts too late, often when working drawings have been completed or nearly so. In other offices, the handling of costs is not so much a matter of control but of estimating.

In any case, the handling of the costs of construction is, in most offices, very rudimentary when compared with the handling of similar problems in, say, the manufacturing industries. It is common practice in such industries for highly paid, imaginative, and talented people to be deeply involved in the costs structure of the products produced. While there are exceptions, this is not usually the case in architecture. Among manufacturing companies, the successful ones anyhow, it would be difficult to find a case in which budgeting, estimating, projections, record keeping, and analysis of costs were not developed to a high level, considered of utmost importance, and handled in a manner consistent with their importance. For the most part, this is not currently true in architecture.

For whatever the reason, the control of costs in architecture, in many cases, is a stepchild of the process until the bidding or construction phase of the work. That this state of affairs can have far-reaching, sometimes disastrous results is well-known. In other chapters of this book, some of the ramifications of this are discussed in considerable detail. That the costs of construction should be shunted into a position of less importance than deserved, forced to give way before design and other considerations and to take a backseat behind the qualitative and quantitative decisions, is also shortsighted—and unnecessary. In fact, the control of the costs of construction can be made into a major, even creative, factor in architectural services intended to produce good buildings. That is what this book is all about.

Cost Control

To start with, it should be pointed out that bringing in jobs within their budgets is only one aspect of cost control, important as it may be. The word "control" is the key to the process and its goals. The idea is that construction costs should not just be estimated—after the fact—but that they should be controlled in the same manner that materials are controlled, or structures, or the site. In this way, the control of costs becomes not just a bookkeeping process, but rather an intrinsic portion of the whole architectural process. In this way, knowledge of costs as they develop and the actions taken to relate the costs to other architectural actions can be brought to bear on the complete problem in a manner that contributes, positively, to the whole architectural process in a meaningful way.

The results of this process can be better design, better planning, more efficient professional services, more satisfied clients. In a phrase, this process creates better buildings that come in within their budgets, not because of some, often arbitrary, late decisions just before or just after bidding, but because one of the tools applied to them from the very beginning of services right through to the end was the creative act of cost control.

Principles of Cost Control

Maybe the best way to get at the principles of cost control is to look at some of the requirements upon which it must be built. Perhaps there are others, but the major requirements would seem to be these:

1. Good cost control requires the talents of trained, intelligent cost experts, who understand the whole architectural and construction process and who approach their work creatively.

2. The second requirement is a body of data and knowledge of costs developed within the office itself and based on its own methods of design and practice.

3. Together with this private knowledge would go access to, and understanding of, published cost data such as indices.

4. There should be knowledge and understanding of the tools and processes available to the cost controller to aid in analyses, calculations, and estimates.

5. And, finally, the cost controllers should be full-fledged members of the architectural team, working closely and on a par with the project architects, designers, and others.

Cost Control Systems

In order to further develop the principles of cost control, it should be pointed out immediately that sufficient knowledge, talent, and proper attitudes toward costs are not enough. If a positive contribution is to be made to architecture, there must be a system of cost control. The rudimentary ideas behind such a system might be enumerated in this manner:

1. Cost control must start at the beginning of architectural services, at the time of programming or of budget estimating, in some cases even before the architect begins his regular services.

2. Cost control must continue throughout the architectural process, from phase to phase.

3. In the early phases, estimates of costs must be made without drawings or other means of determining what the building will be; these estimates will be based upon assumptions, upon past experience, and upon creative visualization of the direction in which the design of the building will probably go.

4. In the early phases, estimates will ordinarily be somewhat rough approximations; as the work goes on, the techniques for estimates, and the estimates themselves, will be refined more and more to reflect decisions made along the way.

5. Before the bidding phase, the estimates will have been refined to a very high degree of accuracy.

6. Cost control must continue during the construction phase, in order to ensure that changes, additions, and the like do not get out of hand and negate the good work done in preceding phases.

7. Cost control ends only with the completion of the building, maybe not even then, since much of what has been done before that time will determine later costs of maintenance and repair.

In the chapters following, all these ideas are discussed and developed.

Determinants of Building Costs

A widespread notion exists, even among clients with considerable experience in construction, that the only things that cause a building to cost more are increasing its size or upgrading the quality of its materials. If this were so, cost control would be considerably easier. In fact, these are only two of the important determinants of costs. Others include the number of people who will use the building and what it is that they will do in it, the location of the building, its site, its shape as well as its size, the time allowable for architectural services and for construction, the construction market, building financing—it would be easy to extend this list even further.

Suffice it to say now, since this subject is discussed fully in another chapter, that considerations such as those enumerated here are obviously determinants of costs of construction, but they are also just as surely determinants of design and other architectural processes that ultimately produce a building that can be incompetent, competent, or great architecture. The point here is that cost control is inextricably a part of the process and can be made to play a creative role in the process. The alternative, that of making design or other decisions and then asking what they will cost, is only too prevalent.

Responsibility for Costs

The total responsibility for the costs of construction usually will be shared by many who participate in the design and construction process, by engineers, draftsmen, estimators, and others. Yet, there is little doubt that the prime responsibility is that of the architect in most cases. While the architect may delegate many of his functions, including that of controlling costs, to others, the fact remains that he ordinarily has the final word, the overall responsibility, and in case of trouble, the prime liability for costs as well as all of the other aspects of his buildings.

In another chapter, the legal implications of the architect's position are discussed in detail. Guidelines are established for realistic appraisal of his position and for safeguards to the extent possible. It should be pointed out, however, that the current trend seems to be for owners of buildings—and the courts—to hold the architect liable for performance in the area of costs, as well as in those of safety and welfare.

One indication that architects have faced up to this responsibility and the trend of court decisions is in the current edition of The Standards of Professional Practice of The American Institute of Architects. This code since 1964 has required the architect, as an ethical obligation, to ". . . maintain an understanding with his client regarding the

project . . . and its estimated probable costs." Further, the standards
have the following to say about costs:

> Where a fixed limit of cost is established in advance of design, the
> architect must determine the character of design construction so as to
> meet as nearly as feasible the cost limit established. He shall keep his
> client informed with competent estimates of probable costs.

This may seem, to some architects and others, to say little more than
what should be expected of any architect or other construction professional. The inclusion of these requirements as an ethical obligation in
the standards of the architect's own professional organization is a giant
step in the direction of improved architectural performance in the area
of construction—and toward renewed confidence among the public and
clients.

In a way, the ethical obligations discussed are thought by some to
be considerably weakened by the remainder of the paragraph in the
standards, which states:

> He [the architect] shall not guarantee the final costs, which will be
> determined not only by the architect's solution of the owner's require-
> ments, but by the fluctuating conditions of the competitive construction
> market.

It should be pointed out that while the first part of the standards
quoted established an ethical obligation of architects to their clients
and is new with this version of the standards, the latter part quoted
has been traditional posture of the architectural profession for many
years, and with good cause. The key consideration in this is that while
the architect controls the work up to a point, he has little or no control
over the construction market and other related factors at the time of
bidding and during construction.

The author of the legal chapter in this book very carefully describes
the implications of the AIA standard contracts, which reflect the ethics
cited above. However, it should be remembered that there are those,
including architects, who believe that the architect has an ethical or
professional obligation that goes a step further than either the ethical
code or the standard contracts. That is, they believe that a competent
architect should be prepared, if the bids come in higher than the maximum amount of money budgeted, to redesign the building at no cost
to the owner, if the reasons for high costs are attributable to the architect's actions rather than those of the owner.

In addition, there are those, especially architects, who believe that
they will never be able to control the costs of construction absolutely,
unless they direct the actual construction. Because it is considered unethical for an architect to act as a building contractor, such proposals
usually take the form of the architect acting as the agent of the owner

to direct the work of the contractors, rather than in the more limited and usual role of supervisor or observer of the construction.

Objections to Cost Control

Among architects, even among some of those who sincerely believe that design within their owners' budgets is an integral part of architectural services, doubts exist about truly complete cost-control systems. Most of these doubts seem to be the "either-or" variety; most take the form of design versus costs or creativity versus businesslike practices, as if these pairs are self-exclusive. With the one, the other becomes very difficult or even impossible. These fears, while possibly very real, are ill-founded if genuine cost-control systems are employed, staffed with top people and practiced in the right way.

What could be worse than being forced into redesign of a project that has been carefully nurtured to a high degree of perfection, only to find that the bids are high? What architect, or other person involved in building design, can forget the agony of being forced to reduce to the minimum all the elements he so carefully designed into his building because the bids are high? Who could enjoy the fragmentation process that must take place at such a time, the process which must tend to reduce the total design effort expended into something that ultimately may resemble what was intended very little, or not at all?

Cost control, as a creative function of the design practice, will reduce such occasions to the minimum, while giving the designer and others involved a firm grip on all the parts of the design process. With such a method, the costs are developed concurrently with the other decisions, and the professionals at work are in control. In the other case they are at the mercy of the costs at a time too late to mold or change them to suit the purpose or to bend them to the will of the design team.

Another fear, or question, often voiced takes the form of a dilemma composed of numbers on the one hand versus judgment on the other. This is easily disposed of; the numbers are necessary for they are the basic informational structure of cost control, but in turn, the numbers make it possible to use judgment based on facts as well as on creative ability or intuition. Cost-control systems make this possible; without these systems, the facts, or at least some of the facts, will not be available.

Methods of Control

Among the widely used methods of cost control, it is probably safe to generalize that the best known, among clients and architects, are the least refined and least dependable, and vice versa.

Far and away, the best-known cost-control method, although it scarcely deserves the title, is the area, or square-foot method. This and other methods are discussed in other places in the present book. However, a few warnings should be hoisted here, and a few principles emphasized.

The area method is widely known, as has been pointed out, especially among those less initiated in architectural processes and the building industry. The method is dangerous, unreliable, and should be avoided at all costs whenever it is possible. However, it is not always possible. The method is easy, quick, and can be used for very rough approximations when very few decisions have been made concerning a building. The method thus probably has a place in the early phases of the architectural process and a continuing life as a check on other methods and as a quick way of comparing costs between locations, building types, or in other ways. When used in comparing costs, care must be taken to translate each area cost into terms which are equivalent with those of the building with which comparison is being made.

While there may be some disagreement about this, even among the authors of this book, the volume method of cost control is probably considered by most professionals as just a cut above the area method and just about as reliable. What has been said about the area method probably applies about equally to the volume method. Another method, which really should be termed "rule-of-thumb" as should the area and volume methods, is the unit-of-use, or unit-use, method.

The unit-of-use method is almost as widely known and applied as the others mentioned, and just as their names define their methods, cost per square foot and cost per cubic foot, the unit-of-use method is based on cost per item—cost per hospital bed, cost per school pupil. Here again, this is not really a refined and reliable method, but it is useful for checks, for early predictions, and for comparisons. Perhaps, in some cases, this method does define the cost picture somewhat better than the others mentioned, since it is tied to the function of the building.

The in-place unit method is widely used and is more accurate than any of the other three mentioned above. This method is more refined than any of the others mentioned, since its basis is in the unit cost of materials or systems, such as the complete erected cost of units of a window-wall system, a square of roofing, or the like. When the unit costs of all the elements have been estimated and added together, the result is a cost picture that is much more accurate than that presented by the other methods.

Another method of cost control, in much less widespread use than the others, is the unit-of-enclosure method. This method, which is far more sophisticated than any of the others, is so important that a complete chapter of this book is devoted to it.

Of course, the best method of all that is at present developed and available is that of taking off the quantities and pricing them, adding all together, assuming the contractor's overhead and profit, tempering all with a knowledge of the construction market and intuition, and finally arriving at a figure for the work. This is not very much of a trick at all, at least in the takeoff-pricing (more of one in the construction market and intuition departments), after the building has been designed, the working drawings and specifications prepared. But the sad fact is that it is too late for even effective cost control, and *creative* control at this juncture is out of the question.

This brings up the question, "Can cost estimates based on quantity takeoffs be made early in the architectural process, even before any drawings have been prepared?" The authors of this book think they can. Further, it will become apparent, upon reading some of the chapters, that there is a degree of agreement among the authors that this is the *only* way creative cost control can be effectively applied to buildings, and further, that a complete cost control system must be founded on such a process, together with provisions for use of the area, volume, and other methods as required for spot checks and other purposes.

Tools, Techniques, and Aids

One of the dilemmas architects and others pose, when speaking of cost control, is that composed of estimating versus control. This one is easily disposed of, since it is no dilemma at all. Estimating is one of the important techniques of cost control, maybe the most important technique of all. Thus, cost control includes estimating in all its ramifications, including quantity surveying. Estimating is not all of cost control, which is the basic fallacy that some fall victim to. The consensus of the authors of this book seems to be that estimating is *the one all-important* facet of a cost-control system. Too often, estimating is the *whole* system, when it should be only one of the techniques or tools.

There are other tools, techniques, and aids available—all of them important to some degree in cost-control systems. Among the more important, and widely known, are CPM and its related systems, computer analysis and its relationships with CPM and the rest of the cost-control system, quantity surveying in its pure, British, form and its modified, American, form—and also in its more widely used form, the American quantity takeoff and pricing system.

All these aids, tools, or techniques are discussed in chapters here. In addition, the system of value engineering, virtually unknown in architecture, has a chapter of its own. Well-established in fields other than architecture, value engineering seems to hold considerable promise in this field. Two other advanced techniques, worth looking into by those of such bent but not discussed here because of their rather esoteric nature, are the techniques of nomograms, widely used in other fields, and the building of cost models. Both hold promise and might be well worth the time of investigation by those possessed of sufficient drive and interest.

A final word or two on the subject of tools, techniques, and aids for cost control might be in order at this stage. And it might be that the final word has not been written on this subject anywhere. New techniques are emerging almost daily. The computer becomes more useful as time goes on, and so it goes. Right now, perhaps the final word, tentatively, might be that the earnest cost controller needs to know all he can about all the tools, techniques, and aids available to him—and to look out for all the new ones coming along—and to use all of them he can to *define* his cost system, *refine* his estimates, and *design* his costs.

Sources of Information

Much information is available to the conscientious cost controller from many places. Much of this can be very valuable to him. None of it can replace his own records of the experience of his own firm; nothing can take the place of his own experience; nothing can compensate for the creative approach to this very important facet of the whole architectural and construction process.

The list of data readily available everywhere starts with the widely disseminated cost indices. The most available, and probably most important of these, include the cost index published periodically by *Engineering News-Record,* the U.S. Department of Commerce indices, and similar data. Many others are published regularly; some of them are not well-known at all. Among these are the index of the Turner Construction Company, which takes into account readings on the current productivity of labor, the efficiency of plant and management of construction, competitive conditions, and a forecast of price trends, most of which other cost indices do not include. At least one architectural office publishes cost indices, Smith, Hinchman and Grylls Associates, Inc. of Detroit. They have done so for more than fifty years. As far as is known, this index is unique among architectural offices. It is difficult to see how the energy, talent, and know-how that goes into the preparation of such an index can do anything but give the office that prepares it a considerable advantage over the offices that do not.

In addition to the cost indices which are published regularly, and disseminated more or less widely, there are systems of cost control, or cost estimating, available. Among the more important of these are the Dow Calculator of the Dodge Division of McGraw-Hill, Inc., the Boeck Building Cost Data Sheets, Means Construction Cost Data, the Marshall Service, and others. Each of these is available for a fee, and each has its positive attributes and the opposite. All are worthy of investigation and may prove to be of some assistance in a cost-control system.

Office Records

None of the cost indices or other information or systems can possibly take the place of records and files, maintained in scrupulous detail, of the jobs that go through an office and any other information on costs, from wherever it may derive. The cost indices and commercial cost systems are meant to be used in partnership with private records, not in lieu of them.

A Last (Introductory) Word, or Two or More

Most of the important facets of creative cost control are discussed, in some depth, in the chapters that follow. Not every author agrees, fully, with every other. There is no "party line" in what follows. Some of the authors tend somewhat to overlap each other, but this is probably permissible since each of the authors comes from a different background, a different set of circumstances, a different-sized office. In the main, it will be found that all the authors agree on the major principles, although no one of them has had any access at all to the work of the others, either in practice or in the preparation of the chapters of this book.

Maybe the introduction to this book should end, before turning the reader over to the experts who follow, with thoughts such as these:

Creative cost control is a system that uses every technique, talent, and tool available to it.

Creative cost control starts with the budgeting phase, or before.

Creative cost control functions as an integral part of the total architectural process.

Creative cost control keeps the architects, and other design professionals, in control of the total process.

Creative cost control makes it possible for decisions to be made, based on full disclosure of the facts, by architect, owner, and all others involved with the process of creating buildings.

PART TWO

Principles of
Cost Control

Charles Luckman, FAIA

Determinants of
Building Costs

For professionals who are facing up to the responsibilities of designing man's total environment in a technologically and sociologically
oriented world, it is imperative that construction costs be handled
in both a "creative" and "controlled" manner.

No longer can such professionals lean upon simple "cost estimating" and the unrealistic and antiquated phrase, often found in contracts, "the architect is not legally responsible for the accuracy of
his estimates," as excuses for not providing clients with realistically
prepared budgets and the subsequent control of these costs. Recent
court decisions have knocked the props out. The most far-reaching
decision recently held that the drawings, "as instruments of service,"
were worthless to the owner because the bids were substantially
above the agreed-upon budget and that, therefore, the owner was
not obligated to pay the architect *any* fee.

This is why I feel professionals must devote the same amount of
imagination to the control of costs as to design.

The word "creative," when used in connection with "cost control,"
means that we must make the budget work for us and not against
us. It's easy to be creative when there is no budget; it is infinitely
more difficult, but equally rewarding, to be creative within a

17

budget. There is no question but that in the new world of architecture
which is on the horizon, we must be creative within the framework of the
budget.

Although the courts have only recently held that we have a legal responsibility to our clients, it has long been the philosophy in our office
that we have a moral responsibility to our clients as binding as any legal
one. Furthermore, proper control of costs will help all architects in
carrying out the mandate that has been handed to us, namely "to make
the world a better place in which people can live." For if we can keep
the costs within the budget, we can then afford to give man a *total*
environment.

Four Needs of Clients

We will find it easier to carry out this mandate if we give the client
the four things he needs from an architect: the cost to be within the
client's own predetermined budget or to be within the budget submitted
by the architect and approved by the client; the basic plan concept
to meet the client's requirements in the most efficient manner; the building, when completed, to have aesthetic merit; the architecture and construction to be done in a manner that will protect the client against
his own inexperience.

In our office, we feel that creative cost control has always been an
important element in the success of our practice and important to the
profession of architecture, whether it be concerned with the design of
only one building or of a complex of buildings. However, now that
the profession has been charged with the responsibility for the design,
or redesign, of man's total environment, creative cost control is of *crucial*
importance.

The architect, in designing a new town, or redesigning the urban
environment of an existing city, has to be the coordinating captain of
a great new team—a team that is expanding in size—made up of many
engineers and other consultants, including environmental specialists, city
planners, lighting and acoustical experts, landscape architects, programmers, accountants, lawyers, and financiers. It is the architect's responsibility to supervise and coordinate the control of costs by *all* these
specialists.

It is also the architect's responsibility to inform his client, at an early
date, of any increased complexity of costs involved in the design of total
environment, how such design adds to the costs of the project, and
the increased costs of providing the "human" elements of architecture,
such as additional volume of space between buildings, landscaping,

benches, flowerpots, fountains, and malls. These increased costs must then be integrated into the total budget.

Once the creative concept has been achieved—within the framework of the budget—all development work thereafter must be *controlled* in cost. For example, an architect traditionally makes a cost estimate when he finishes the schematic phase of his design. The validity of this first estimate depends upon the way in which the design development drawings are controlled after that. The detail drawings and specifications must follow the schematic concept in all its basic premises. The space allotment has to stay the same, the quantity of materials has to be identical, and a "standard" item on the schematic drawings must not appear on the preliminary drawing as a "custom" item.

The same meticulous care has to be exercised, and similar controls applied, when progressing from preliminary drawings to final working drawings. Controlling the specifications and details going into the drawings represents the difference between keeping within the budget and going beyond it.

The client and the architect must both be controlled. If the client wants to add to the building, or to use more expensive materials, the architect must promptly advise him exactly how much more each of these changes will add to the approved budget. This will enable the client to make a considered judgment—based on facts and figures— before deciding whether or not the changes are to be made.

Once the budget has been established, and such changes are made, one of the most important services the architect can provide the client as the "owner's representative" is to keep a running record that will promptly and regularly inform the client about the current status of costs as compared with the budget.

The coming "second" post-World War II population explosion and the accompanying building boom, when added to the current demand for a better living environment for everyone, provide the architect with challenges and opportunities of a scale never even dreamed of before. If housing is to be more than "shelter," the architect will have to have an even greater knowledge of costs, and an even sharper control of these costs.

The age of technology, while creating part of the architect's problems, also provides him with some of the tools to solve them. For example, the computer will play an increasingly important role in the architect's life; it will be used for designing, drafting, detailing, research, programming, and large-scale planning. However, the computer will accomplish great things for the architect only if he knows how to use it and how to program it. If not properly programmed, computer time will add to the overall cost rather than reduce it, because the computer "readout" is only as good as the material and information put into it.

Computers in Cost Control

Computers also play an important role in cost control through CPM, which was developed for the express purpose of determining the optimum sequence of events in design, planning, and scheduling of construction projects. It was found that the computer was ideal for operating such a method. CPM controls costs in two ways: by determining the sequential logic of building design and construction operations, and by the regular updating of the project to evaluate progress, determine expenditures to date, and provide for any revised manpower schedules. It also emphasizes the interrelated dependencies of all the operations that make up the project and points up the "areas" that are critical. (An area is critical if a delay in it would cause a delay in the entire project.)

Having examined the need for creative cost control, and having acknowledged the immeasurable challenges and opportunities facing the architect in the future, we shall now examine the various factors that determine costs, how costs can be controlled, how costs vary under different conditions, and finally, how these separate determinants all come together to create the total concept.

People

Architecture is for people. Before explaining why people are a construction-cost determinant, I'd like to present a bit of my publicly expressed philosophy:

> Surely we are not to be judged, or judge ourselves, merely by our capacity to use brick and mortar, glass and steel. Rather, our use of material, like the use of our skills, should be measured only by the yardstick of human needs and aspirations. Unless these are served, a building, no matter how beautiful, will deny the importance of human scale by failing to consider that buildings are for people—and must therefore be planned, designed, and built to embody the desires and dignity of the human being. This is what I term the "humanization of architecture."

People are considered a construction-cost determinant because, when a budget for a building is being prepared, the way the building is to be used by people and the number of people who will be using the building affect the costs. The higher the personnel density, the greater will be the requirements for increased facilities needed to maintain user efficiency, productivity, and comfort. Thus, the higher the density, the higher the costs.

The use of a building will determine the selection of materials, finishes, circulation patterns, maintenance methods and materials, number and types of spaces, the use of those spaces, and other important characteristics of the building. Naturally, there will be differences in space designed for secretarial use, for executive offices, for industrial plants, for homes, for schools, for hospitals, or for other specific uses.

A study,[1] made a few years ago, shows how personnel density affects construction costs. The example analyzed the cost breakdown of an industrial building, a 200,000 sq ft single-story building to be used as a warehouse without manufacturing operations.

This building would house a minimum number of people: twenty men in the warehouse, three men and five women in the office. This gave a low personnel-density factor of one person per 8,000 sq ft. The design and budget were minimum; the cost per sq ft, not including the cost of design and an allowance for contingencies, was established at an index of 100.

The next step of the study changed the same building into a light manufacturing plant with 700 employees and a personnel density of about one person per 285 sq ft. Although this new concept of a manufacturing building actually retained the original building concept, with only a few changes, the cost more than doubled to a new index of 254.4, not including professional fees and contingency allowance. The bulk of the cost increase went for additional mechanical, electrical, and site work, all related directly to the personnel density of the building.

The third part of the study increased the number of people to 1,000, or a personnel density of about one person per 200 sq ft. Despite the fact that the building concept remained essentially the same as the basic structure, the cost jumped to an index of almost 340, exclusive of fees and contingencies. Once again the increased costs were largely in electrical, mechanical, and site work, rather than architectural or structural. Once again, the increased costs were directly related to the increase in personnel density.

So it would be in all other types of buildings; increases in personnel density would also increase the cost of the buildings, and once again, the increases would be mainly attributable to additional mechanical and electrical work required by increased personnel density.

Building Location

If the site of a building has not been predetermined, feasibility studies are of utmost importance in creative cost control, and often the architect will prepare such studies for his client.

[1] Frank L. Whitney, "Personnel Density," *Architectural Record,* pp. 155–158, March, 1961.

These studies are of compelling significance because the location of the site greatly influences the ultimate cost of the building. The variations in costs are often caused by a composite of the influences of climate, codes, and construction-labor practices. The time of the year in which bids are taken can cause substantial variations in price; in some areas cold weather means difficult working conditions and therefore a loss of production. This results in higher bids. As a corollary, bids taken in the summer may also be high because the contractors are busy. Building costs tend to be higher in large cities because of competition for available construction labor, rigid building codes, and strong labor unions. Away from the city, costs tend to decrease.

Factors to be considered and weighed before a final decision is made concerning the location of a building include cost of land in the city contrasted with cost of suburban land; cost of building in each area; availability of water, gas, electricity, and sewerage systems; preparation of the site, including landscaping; availability of public transportation; cost of adequate parking; quality of the land in case of foundation problems. Will there be rock to be blasted, low water tables, or other water problems to be faced?

On a predetermined site, the exact location of the building on the site can influence the cost. The cost of constructing a building which abuts another on one side is higher than the cost of erecting a building which is exposed on all sides. Our cost analysis for the Prudential Center in Boston showed the client that it was cheaper to buy four adjacent acres and demolish the old Mechanics Hall than to build around it.

As a further example, it may be that free land for college sites, if remote, can result in cost penalties of untold amounts of money over the years. One fact to be determined immediately is how much grading will be necessary to prepare the land as a campus, how much cut and fill? In this connection, on several of the California state college sites, the "free" land has turned out to cost millions of dollars.

How about access streets? Perhaps the campus is alongside a freeway, but how much will access streets from the freeway to the campus cost, if they are not already in place?

Campus master-planning architects must remember to add to their overall budget the costs of bicycle paths, bicycle racks, and security measures to prevent the stealing of bicycles. The car ratio at the University of California at Santa Barbara campus has now reached 1 car to every $1\frac{1}{2}$ students—and two-thirds of the students also use bicycles.

Also, architects planning colleges must consider how the academic plan affects the cost of the campus, for example, the comparative costs of an urban vertical college versus the costs of a suburban college treated as a single campus with centralized buildings, such as library and laboratories, versus the costs of a suburban college treated as many separate schools with complete facilities for each of its disciplines, such as law, medicine, architecture, and fine arts. All these must be studied to see which type of college best accommodates the academic master plan and the available funds.

Almost every client underbuys when he is purchasing land. It is the architect's responsibility to point out to the client the potential future savings that he can make by buying an adequate amount of land at the outset. This is true when purchasing land for an industrial building, a hospital, a school, a new town, or for any project where the feasibility study indicates a potential need for additional land for future expansion.

Building Size and Conformation

At the very beginning of his services to the client, when an architect creates a design for a building, he must consider how the size and configuration of the building will affect the cost. For example, in the design of an office building containing 200,000 sq ft, great variations in costs can occur because of the various shapes the building may take when enclosing the space. The architect may study this most readily by looking at the amount of required perimeter wall for enclosing the 200,000 sq ft.

For example, the shapes that might be used and the number of lineal feet needed to enclose one level of such a 200,000 sq ft building are as follows:

	Lin ft
Circle	1,578
Hexagon	1,650
Square	1,792
Rectangle	1,934
L-shape	2,200

This leads us to a number of comparisons; for example, the difference between the walls for the square and those of the L-shape is over 400 lin ft. Thus the L-shape requires about 25 percent more wall area than the square to enclose the same amount of area and has more corners which add to the cost. The circle requires the least wall area, but the increased cost of constructing curvilinear walls eliminates it from practical consideration.

Other than the circle, hexagon, or square, the rectangular shape encloses the required wall with less wall than any other shape. The rectangle is less costly to build than the L-shape, hexagon, or circle and has the advantage of lending itself to the best ratio obtainable between gross and net floor area.

The next factor to consider is the arrangement of levels to develop 200,000 sq ft. Obviously, this area can be placed on one floor, or ten levels of 20,000 sq ft each, or any number of combinations, each with a different cost factor. In addition, it must be recognized that local zoning regulations and building codes may curtail flexibility to a certain extent. Another important consideration in determining the building size and conformation, especially in a major city, is the land value and necessary return to the investing builder and developer.

Construction Type and Quality

Differences in the types of construction used and the quality of the materials going into buildings can result in a wide latitude of costs. This requires a very careful study of the client's budget and strict attention to cost control, with particular reference to quality.

However, when any building is studied, three degrees of quality—minimum, average, and excellent—might be assumed; the cost variations between buildings of the three qualities will surprise most architects and shock most of their clients.

In all three degrees of quality, a building may have the same basic structure, since costs in this area of construction vary only in a limited way. In contrast, there are areas in which the range of costs is quite large, for example, structural systems for ceilings; plumbing and sprinklers; heating, ventilating, and air conditioning; electrical work; site work. Also in connection with elevators in a multistory office building, the range of costs between minimum quality and excellent quality is very great.

In our office, we prepare a cost-analysis summary of each building—separated into minimum, average, and excellent quality—showing the relative amounts of the total building costs attributable to various portions of the work. We use these cost analyses as aids in explaining projects to our clients.

A start toward cost control has been made by the School Construction Systems Development project. In this experiment, the attempt has been made to develop an integrated system of standard school building components which will offer architects design flexibility in meeting the changing program needs of individual schools; reduce the cost of school construction and give better value for the school building dollar in terms of function, environment, initial cost, and maintenance; and reduce the time needed to build a school.

From the SCSD project and similar work, it would seem that architects can look toward use of more preassembled systems in various building types which will help to reduce on-site construction costs. These new systems will, in all likelihood, be checked out by computer before they are specified to determine that the products of different manufacturers will fit together when they arrive on the site.

In our office, design and materials are considered to be synonymous. In fact, to achieve "humanization" of architecture, for which we constantly strive, our designs are frequently the outgrowth of materials we want to use; in all cases, the design is strongly influenced by the material selection. Furthermore, it is not possible to keep design and materials separate and still stay within the owner's budget.

Custom versus Standard Elements

A most important factor in the control of costs is the decision whether to use custom or standard elements in a building. The architect, who has the ethical and legal responsibility to stay within the client's budget, must be knowledgeable enough—and frank enough—to explain to the client how much more expensive a building will be if custom elements are used instead of standard elements.

Custom elements, in most cases, have to be tailor-made, while standard elements are usually readily available from stock. The installation of custom elements will generally take more skill and time than the installation of standard elements.

After having been apprised of the differences in costs between custom and standard elements, which the architect has presented to him, the client can then make a realistic decision on which to use.

The single most important aspect to guard against, in this respect, is that as the drawings move from concept to preliminary to final working drawings, they are *controlled* so that a custom item does not "accidentally" replace a standard item.

Time and Timing

Although it is very obvious that time and timing are very important cost determinants in the construction of a building, the architect has the responsibility of making certain that the client realizes just how important they really are.

In a perfect world, the budget would be set; the architect would create his design and the owner approve it; bids would be secured from general contractors; the selected general contractor would get bids from the subcontractors and choose those that best qualify. All construction materials would be purchased in a buyer's market, thereby assuring low prices and on-time delivery. The work would start at a seasonably favorable time and proceed without delay until the building is completed on schedule, the certificate of occupancy obtained immediately, and the owner or tenants move in and start using the space.

However, in our imperfect world, the architect must establish a realistic schedule for designing, planning, and constructing the building and adhere to it closely. More often than not, he will use CPM to assist him in maintaining his schedule.

The earlier the program development goes ahead, the smaller the increase in expenses should be, and the sooner the owner will start to get a return on his money. As the work is expedited, the schedule being met or bettered, the easier it is to keep ahead of increasing construction costs, including labor, materials, and money.

When it is necessary for a project to go out of phase, the architect must know when to advise his client to order his foundation work, when to order his steel for framing, and when to have it delivered to the site; the architect should complete the contract documents while the foundations are being readied and the steel is being delivered. The architect should also know when to buy lead items in time for delivery when needed. It is incumbent upon the architect to allow enough time for full development of the items on the job schedule until the time when the selected general contractor can take over the prime responsibility.

The Construction Market

Construction, which has often been called the largest fabricating industry in the country, has a great effect on the nation's economy. New construction accounts for about 10 percent of the gross national product, and maintenance and repair usually account for another 4 or 5 percent. Thus it's easy to see that as construction goes, so goes the economy of the United States.

Since the end of World War II, construction has set a new record each year. In 1965, work-in-place amounted to about $70 billion. The F. W. Dodge Company predicts that by 1975 the construction market will be double its current size.

This forecast is based upon the second post-World War II population explosion—predicted for the next decade—and the accompanying building boom. By the year 1975, population in the United States will increase to a total of 226 million; household units will reach the 70 million mark, 12 million more than we have today; and housing starts will have reached an annual rate of more than 2 million units. There will also be a surging demand for more commercial and industrial buildings, schools, hospitals, and recreational facilities. In addition, government programs, based upon dynamic, sociological changes, will add to the tempo of the construction program.

Alexander the Great died at the age of thirty-two, but no one then thought that he had died at a premature age. Today, the biblical "three-score years and ten" has become a reality, and we now face not just the problem of geriatrics, but the problem of vastly increased leisure time brought about by the seeming inevitability of the four-day week. Within fifteen years, three-fourths of our families will have the need for a "weekend hideaway."

In the future, because of the need for housing for the over-sixty-five group and for leisure housing, new concepts of cost control and new concepts of construction will have to be devised by architects to make this "special" housing economically feasible.

The labor force will increase by 1.8 percent per year between now and 1970. After that, rate of increase will be 1.6 percent per year. This will result in an extra 6 million workers by 1975. These people will make themselves felt not only as producers but as consumers. Thus it will be necessary to continue maximum output in our industrial plants, and plant capacity must continue to expand.

As a result of the expansion of the residential market, and also of the commercial and industrial building markets, there will be a stimulation of the market for utilities and institutional buildings. By the mid-1970s the demand for schools will be similar to that of the first post-World War II "baby boom." Medicare will result in the need for more and more hospital facilities, and the Great Society will bring about the construction of more medical facilities, housing, and recreational areas.

What happens in the construction market will deeply affect architects and their control of costs. From a broad point of view over the next ten years, there will be almost unlimited opportunity for architects able to measure up to the new scale of architecture—the creation of the total environment for man; for architects able to take advantage of the technological changes; for architects able to use the computer for design, drafting, programming, and large-scale planning in new towns, redesigned urban areas, and civic centers; and for architects able to use the new preassembled systems to expedite building construction.

Despite the great opportunities that will be presented to architects to contribute to the welfare of our country and the great technological advances being made, archaic building codes and zoning regulations and the demands of the building trades for increased wages, made in spite of the continuation of inefficient construction methods, will act as a drag on the future progress of the building industry.

For these reasons, architects must strive even harder to be creative in the control of costs. Their efforts must compensate to a certain extent for increased material costs, increased money costs, and increased labor costs.

Architects must be aware of the reputation of general contractors and subcontractors with whom they work. They must know, or be able to determine, which contractors to recommend in various parts of the country.

As leaders of the building team, which is continually becoming larger to cope with the ever-expanding comprehensive services of the profession, architects should take the lead in establishing some sort of coordinating council on costs among all of the design, planning, and construction professionals. Such an organization could collect and disseminate information not only on what makes buildings cost what they do, but why.

Quantity Purchasing

Quantity purchasing, when used in the sense of creative cost control, refers to design details that are repeated throughout a building in order to make it economical to buy in quantity. A good designer can create details that will be aesthetically interesting and, at the same time, repetitive. The alternative to this is a large number of individual details, used in lesser numbers. This will inevitably increase the cost of the building. For example, refinement of a detail on a door buck could save as much as $1.20 per door when repeated throughout a large building. In a large apartment or office building, the savings can obviously be quite substantial.

Other examples in which quantity purchasing can reduce costs include various elements of hardware, electrical fixtures and outlets, and other similar products which can be bought in quantity and still provide a handsome building.

Financing

The financing of the construction of a building, or of an urban redevelopment project, is an important determinant of cost control. Whether a joint venture, an owner-client, or any other combination of ownership, experienced handling of the financial negotiations in borrowing money for the project can result in an appreciable saving in the cost of the building, for interest rates, takeout costs, and interim financing are all very real costs of building. In this connection, it is the architect's responsibility to project costs to the date that the financing becomes available and to conrol them in the interim.

The architect's proper preparation of financing drawings, done with thoroughness and care, can be most helpful to his client.

The architect should be knowledgeable about the money market because his ability to participate in financing discussions can be of substantial consequence to the client.

The reputation of the architect for the accuracy of his drawings, and his control of costs, frequently influences financial institutions in their decisions to make money available at a favorable rate of interest.

This same reputation and ability will be of great advantage to the architect when he is representing a client who wants to borrow money for a government project, whether local, state, or Federal. When HUD (Housing and Urban Development) and FHA provide money for a large project, they require the architect to submit a good concept in which the control of costs is completely apparent.

Putting the Determinants Together

As stated earlier, it is imperative that the architect handle construction costs in both a creative and in a controlled manner. He has no choice but to keep costs within the budget, if he is going "to make the world a better place in which people can live."

The combination of cost factors that have to be controlled by the architect on a given project depends upon the particular circumstances with which he is faced. In general, however, the cost factors that have been discussed are to be found in every project.

Once the schematics for a project have been completed and approved, the architect must *control* costs during the preparation of the preliminary drawings. He must do this to ensure that the details and specifications on the schematics are not enlarged upon during the preparation of drawings. He must use the same meticulous care when going from preliminary drawings to working drawings. If the architect does not control what goes on the drawings, he will end up with enlarged spaces, custom rather than standard elements, and more details than originally specified—all or any of which will cause the project to exceed the agreed-upon budget.

The architect, by devoting as much imagination to cost control as to design, will make it possible for man once more to have his full measure of *freedom*, of *dignity*, of *purpose*—in a total environment in which his family can enjoy a full life.

Architects owe it not only to their clients but to themselves—and to the future of architecture—to eliminate the public's widely held belief that "architects make buildings cost more." When the day comes that architects have proved their ability to produce fine work within a budget—on houses or hospitals, on cabanas or colleges, on new towns or redesigned cities—we shall vastly increase our participation in the total volume of the construction of man's total environment.

THREE

King Royer and Brad Howes

Cost Control
for the Life
of Buildings

An owner, when he buys a building, purchases only a portion of what he requires. The building does represent a large part of the cost necessary to provide shelter and other needs; the remainder of the cost is in the annual costs of labor, material, insurance, and other items necessary throughout the life of the building. If, as is usual, a building loan is being repaid over a long period, the owner analyzes the cost of the project in terms of annual cost. The original cost of the building, by itself, is not important. If the owner uses his own funds, he expects to gain a return on his total investment as great as though he were a lender.

The architect, therefore, should be familiar with the method by which he may transfer costs between original building costs and other annual costs, reducing the annual cost for the benefit of the client. The best source of information for the architect is the client who has bought a number of buildings, has operated them with an adequate cost-control system, and therefore knows the types of construction which are economical. Such a client is a source of cost information which the architect may utilize for the benefit of less informed clients.

Original/Annual Cost Ratio

What is the equivalent, immediate cost of a dollar-a-year maintenance or tax expense? This depends on the rate of interest paid by the client (or income foregone) and his tax situation.

Interest Rate

The applicable interest rate, in general, will not be the mortgage interest rate on the building. If an additional feature on a building will cost more initially but will lower the maintenance cost, the applicable interest rate is on the funds for the *addition,* not on the original loan. Usually loans are obtained for as large an amount as possible, and the lender is not disposed to increase the loan because of an added detail. If the original request for a loan is based on a justification of annual cost, it may be that a reduced annual cost will increase the amount of money available, but this is unusual. It must normally be assumed that the additional funds will come from the owner—either by his obtaining additional funds or by his reducing the amount he would recover for other investment from the mortgage money lent to him.

This rate of interest, therefore, is the amount the owner could obtain on his additional funds if invested in another project with the same risk—equivalent to a second mortgage. Furthermore, by increasing his investment, the owner may be foregoing capital gains, but the income he gains may be ordinary income. A 20 percent interest rate is not unusual for commercial second mortgages, to the extent they are marketable at all; if a capital-gains income is lost, the interest rate to the owner would have to be twice as great to pay the additional taxes, or 40 percent interest.

If the owner has unlimited credit, however, and is not a profit-making organization, the circumstances are entirely different. A public agency, for example, pays the same interest rate on its original loan as on additions to it. If a bond issue is involved, the effective interest rate may be as low as 3 percent. Consequently, it is not to be expected that the economical type of construction would be the same for the two kinds of owners.

To take a concrete situation, suppose that you have an item on a building which will cost the owner $100 more if installed. What is the annual cost of this investment, considering "cost" as the amount his profit will be reduced? Assume he could invest $100 of his own money elsewhere and obtain $20 per year in capital gains, of which he could retain $15 per year after taxes, at the same risk. The risk, in general, is proportional to the equity an owner has in a development—by making an improvement you not only are increasing the *size* of the job, but are increasing his *equity*—thereby increasing his risk. After all, he isn't even sure he can use the building when completed; any future income is a hope, and the increase you have made, which does not increase the gross income, is even less certain. If the corporation, let us assume, is in the 40 percent tax bracket also, then if the corporation increases its profit $33.75, dividends are increased $22.50; and of this dividend, the owner retains $15. In other words, a $100 addition to the project must save over $33.75 annually to be economical. The original/annual cost ratio is 3:1.

The risk of loss, rather than profit, in the project must also be considered. The ratio, in this case, depends on more complicated factors—particularly what the loss may eventually be charged against. It is unlikely that the advantages of the added construction would be any greater than with a profit job.

Private versus Public Buildings

The illustration above is an extreme one; it is only here to show that no assumptions can be made without investigation. Public buildings can readily justify a 33:1 original/annual cost ratio, in comparison with the 3:1 ratio above. Other differences are that public buildings are depreciated at rates independent of income tax considerations; maintenance costs would be higher on public buildings; insurance rates may be lower and utility rates less. Public schools are frequently in an even more extreme position. Due to school-taxation limitations which permit bond issues for new construction while severely limiting taxation for current maintenance expenses, an original/annual cost ratio as high as 50:1 may be advisable—for practical, if not for economic, considerations.

Few owners analyze costs in such detail. The architect, in order to justify the construction or to determine the most economical construction, may make such an analysis or request it of his client.

Maintenance Costs

Unfortunately, maintenance costs are seldom available in the same detail as are construction costs. Owners may assume that their own maintenance force is of a fixed size and therefore that with minor variations in construction there is no variation in labor cost. This is not a reasonable assumption, unless it is actually known that the work to be done is less than the capacity of the work force that will actually be engaged, that is, if it is definite that time will be wasted. Otherwise, adding a small item of work may require employment of another man, who will be underemployed in the job. The reasonable assumption is that the cost of maintenance is the cost of actual labor required—and to make no assumptions, in advance, about an unchanging work force.

Maintenance Conference

When a project is to be designed for a client with an existing maintenance organization, the person in charge of maintenance should be consulted early in the design. Line supervisors in charge of operations often have little to do with building maintenance, and it is not unusual for the same design errors to be repeated on successive buildings. Such obvious errors as specifying toilet paper and towel holders which do not use the paper that is standard with the organization will occasionally occur.

The maintenance supervisor, however, is frequently inclined to request building features which minimize or simplify maintenance, without regard to actual economic cost. Such items should be first discussed between the architect's representative and the maintenance supervisor privately, not in an open meeting, so that the architect will not be forced into agreement or disagreement on items until he has had a chance to study the matter and to obtain information from the supervisor without appearing to cross-examine him.

Weather Protection

Construction details necessary for protection against atmospheric water are generally accepted; the extra cost involved is incurred in the inspection necessary to ensure that the plans are followed. Often, however, details are designed for initial appearance, with little regard for possible weathering and discoloring, as in the use of windowsills flush with the outside face of walls and other details which allow water to flow down the face of buildings or into the walls.

Masonry and concrete shrink after being placed, and no care in workmanship can avoid a possibility of leaks due to this shrinkage. For this reason, it is recommended that all masonry and concrete structure be considered porous and that flashing be provided at the bottom of walls which may leak into finished spaces. Good practice is well established, but there is a tendency to use short cap flashings stuck into exterior walls rather than through-wall flashings in lower portions of walls, often with resulting water damage. Leakage through walls may occur very infrequently in normal construction, not because the walls are tight but because water runs down through the walls and into the ground; this same construction, used where the lower portion of the wall is over a finished space, shows its faults quickly. In such locations, the source of the leak may be difficult to determine; thus responsibility may not be accepted by the contractor.

Partially Complete Construction

Some types of construction make it possible for a less expensive method to be used initially but increase maintenance work during the first few years of use. This maintenance work is currently deductible as repairs on income tax returns. For example, asphaltic concrete is normally laid in two layers—a base course and a finish course, totaling about 2 in. in thickness. By laying the base course slightly thicker than usual and omitting the finish course, the pavement is sufficient for several years; when it begins to need repairs, the second course is applied. The original construction would have to be paid for out of past profits and depreciated over a period of years; the same material applied later is charged against current profits before taxes—or in effect, is depreciated all at one time. There may be no difference in taxes in the long run, but tax payments are delayed a number of years, and original cost is reduced.

Other Tax Factors

The architect, in performing his services, is also designing the income tax deductions for years to come. If portions of leased construction are designed specifically for a tenant, as is often the case, these portions may generally be depreciated on the assumption they will be required by only that tenant, not on the basis of total life. (Recently, a contrary decision was made: if renewal of the lease is "reasonably certain," the building life must be used.) This may make a difference in allowable depreciation of central air-conditioning systems in shopping centers as compared with individual store units. The central systems are not designed for particular tenants, and therefore their life is determined by actual life; the individual system is designed for a particular tenant and has no value as an installed unit after the lease has expired. The same reasoning would apply to longer-life components of the building, such as partitions and ceilings.

The attainment of maximum depreciation rates for tax purposes is often essential for developers; taxes are not necessarily paid out of cash profits, and it could therefore be necessary to borrow money to pay them. This comes about because with a large proportion of the project covered by a mortgage, profits may go into amortization, leaving no cash to pay income taxes.

Ideally, therefore, depreciation will equal profits so there is no tax liability. In one case, the owners of a concrete-frame building were given a depreciation rate so high it exceeded profits, and the depreciation rate was reduced to avoid a loss situation.

1411347 *Traffic Conditions*

A building needs to be checked specifically to find all possible sources of high maintenance cost created by the people and automobiles using the area. Features which appear useful on the plans or in the completed building may be entirely valueless because of interference by traffic. For example, narrow strips of lawn, such as between sidewalks and parking lanes, are expensive to maintain and nearly impossible to keep alive, because of heavy foot traffic. If grass interferes with the passage of pedestrians, it will be trampled, and maintenance crews will eventually pave these areas.

In areas where parking is at a premium (and this is nearly everywhere), it should be expected that drivers will occupy all available space. Grassed areas must be protected by fences; it may be necessary to install posts between the columns of exposed canopies to prevent cars from driving through them. This is particularly important in the neighborhood of sports stadiums. Near driveways there should also be no construction which can be damaged by vehicles; columns should be set back from drives, and masonry walls protected by corner guards.

The destructiveness of the public, particularly where persons must wait at one location, such as at a bus stop, should not be underestimated. When whittling was a more common leisure sport than it is today, power poles at small-town intersections had to be replaced because of damage by pocketknives. They were then covered with sheet metal, as if to protect young trees from rabbits. School children can flatten sheet-metal downspouts and even break tops of cast-iron drains. Under heavy traffic, concrete or terrazzo stairs not protected by steel-edged strips will break off in pieces, leaving disfiguring markings.

Water and Gas Distribution

Construction costs can also be reduced at the expense of increased annual costs by installing as small a part as possible of utility distribution systems as a part of the construction work. Since water and sanitary drainage are normally a function of public agencies, it is to the advantage of the owner that public agencies install these facilities, even if the financial arrangement made does not necessarily appear to be profitable on the basis of total cost; tax considerations may override greater total cost. Tax payments are expenses, and an arrangement which will transfer cost from construction to tax accounts is to the benefit of the owner. This may require individual meters, and even a complicated right-of-way description, if a city is to install public lines on private property.

Because of the tax consideration previously outlined, the owner should not attempt to go into the utility business by distribution of utilities bought wholesale, unless an analysis which considers the tax effect is made. Also, the utility companies often use nonunion labor, and even if union, this labor is more skilled at the work and is less costly per man-hour than is construction labor.

When the architect is to provide supporting structure for utility lines, he should fully investigate not only the construction preferred by the utility company, but the minimum construction they actually require. For example, years ago transformers were filled with inflammable oil and had to be installed in substantial fireproof vaults; now noninflammable fluids are used, and such vaults are not necessary. Nevertheless, many vaults are installed by repeating old designs. Gas lines do not need to be run underground merely because they are the property of the utility company; the company can run them above ground or in buildings.

Depreciation Schedule

There are three common ways of determining the life of buildings for depreciation purposes: by a single life for the entire structure, by using different lives for each portion, such as structure, painting, heating equipment, or by a combination of this latter method with lease life for those items which can be shown to pertain to a particular lease.

The separation of the project into parts for determination of depreciation lives, or preparation of the depreciation schedule, can usually be done from the records of division of the work for payment purposes. The architect should find out what is needed, however, and assure himself that the specifications are definite enough that he can require the necessary breakdown by the contractor. Care must be taken, also, that a weighted breakdown used for payment purposes does not cause the owner to receive a misleading cost breakdown which will reduce his allowed depreciation. For example, when making a cost breakdown, the contractor will charge as much as possible to the first work to be done, often the site work. But the owner can only depreciate this portion of the work over a very long period if at all; it is to the owner's advantage to have the mechanical portion of the work, particularly equipment, valued as high as possible. This work, if installed last, may be reported by the contractor at cost or even lower.

Fire Insurance

Consideration of the fire insurance rate on a building being designed is of special importance because the annual cost of insurance, unlike other costs, can be accurately forecast and because apparently minor details of design or workmanship can greatly affect the insurance rate. In addition, the architect is seldom notified of the penalties assessed on his design and has no readily available method of determining what should be done.

Rating Bureaus

Insurance rates for larger buildings are set not by the insurance companies but by a separate company organized for that purpose. This company, a rating bureau, serves nearly all companies in its state, providing rates for particular buildings on request, based on examination of the plans and specifications and of the construction itself. This bureau itself determines which items affect the rate, independent of the national underwriters' organization, and it is not required to conform to any other standards.

The rating bureau does not define standards of construction as such but assigns risk values to differing kinds of buildings and to different details. There is no necessary relationship between this bureau and the National Building Code, which is used by many cities, or any city code. Consequently, construction which does not comply with the National Code in some particular may be assessed a lower insurance rate than other types of construction which do comply. Sprinklered buildings, for example, receive the lowest rate regardless of structure, but the National Code does not mention a modification of area requirements if the building is sprinklered. Noncombustible construction, therefore, may not be used in some large buildings, even if sprinklered.

The National Code is recommended by the National Board of Fire Underwriters, controlled by the same insurance companies who use the rating bureau for determination of rates.

The bureaus use a *schedule book* and a *rule book* to determine rates; these books set the adjustment to be made to the rate for various kinds of construction details. These books are available only to insurance companies and agents; as a practical matter, the insurance companies themselves may not have a copy. The copies examined by the writers were not copyrighted. Lack of a copyright would indicate either that it is intended for free reuse (the National Building Code is uncopyrighted) or that it is a private publication and the issuing office does not want a copy available to the public. The above publications are apparently intended to be private. (In one case, the state office of an insurance company was provided with a copy of the schedule book, but the information on all buildings except those with wood floors and roofs was omitted.)

The architect can approach these agencies only if armed with a proposed plan as representative of the owner. He will probably have to be quite persistent to find out the actual changes in the rate. One bureau, in response to a request for information, replied, "We are not prepared to furnish material which will be used as a basis for articles for magazines or professional journals"; in general, the complications of their system of rating are emphasized, and they may claim to be unable to determine the effect of construction changes on the insurance rate. Part of this complication is due to the results of changes in construction given in the schedules as cents per hundred dollars of insurance, but this results in a rate which is later cut by percentages for various other factors; that is, some corrections are in cents per hundred and some corrections are percentages applied to the rate. Once a complete computation is made, however, correction for minor construction changes can be readily made.

Method of Rating

Buildings are first given a base rate according to construction—whether fireproof, noncombustible, or combustible—and according to degree of fire protection offered by the local fire department. Cities have a numerical rating which expresses the estimated efficiency of the fire department, and a different insurance rate is given for each numerical fire-department rating. The base rate is also dependent on occupancy and on the number of tenants occupying the building. The occupancy rate is determined by the most dangerous use being made of the building or of part of it.

A "building" is an area similar to that defined by building codes—an area set off by fire walls or by separation of structures—but the rating bureaus use a less rigorous definition of walls necessary to separate one building from another. In general, separation for their purposes may be obtained by structure which is less expensive than that required by building codes. "Buildings" may therefore be one size so far as building officials are concerned and a different size for determination of fire insurance rates.

After the base rate is determined, protection and contents are considered; there are numerous corrections applied, for example, for columns if fireproofed; for exterior columns, independently of interior columns; for size of building; for type of ceiling; for existence of wood paneling; and for partitions in various places, such as around openings in floors and around areas with furnaces. If the building is sprinklered, an entirely different schedule is used, and the rating is made by different persons.

Applications

In general, it is not economical to make changes in design to gain a lower insurance rate; the least expensive construction allowed by local codes is usually the least expensive from the standpoint of annual cost. However, there are a number of situations which may make a design unusual in this regard, such as:

1. A high-risk occupancy in all or part of the structure, where cutting the building up with division walls may reduce the rate materially.

2. A high-risk occupancy or several occupancies in part of an area, such as a paint shop adjoining a department store. The paint store rate would apply to the whole area if no separation were made.

3. Where contents are of high value, and the owner of the building directly or indirectly pays insurance on the contents. Since the structure affects the rate on contents as well as on structure, the rate saving on contents may be several times the saving on the building itself.

4. Necessary changes in structure to provide additional fire protection are of small cost. For example, a masonry bearing wall for steel joists need be only as high as the bearing of the joists, according to code requirements. By filling in with masonry between the joists, $2\frac{1}{2}$ in. high, the wall becomes a division wall for insurance purposes (If the deck is noncombustible, a parapet wall is not usually necessary).

5. Original/annual cost ratio is unusually high, such as for public construction already mentioned.

If there is no applicable building code, as in public work or in isolated areas, the most economical design from a standpoint of insurance rates would probably be similar to that required by the National Building Code, but sprinklered buildings would be more frequently used in multistory buildings. Since by the use of sprinklers, insurance rates are cut much further than by use of structural improvements, sprinkler cost is often compensated for by the saving in structure, and the insurance saving is a welcome by-product. Concrete structure is expensive for roof construction but is often required, by codes, for large buildings. The National Code allows the building official some discretion in this regard, but he is not always willing to exercise it. Substitution of steel joists and noncombustible roof construction will usually save enough money to pay for a sprinkler system to serve not only the roof structure but additional areas as well.

There is a tendency to install plaster ceilings, as compared with non-combustible acoustical or panel glass-fiber ceilings, where not needed for code purposes because of a conviction that there is a saving in fire insurance rates. In modern construction, a plaster ceiling is seldom useful as a fire membrane because of the openings required for recessed lighting and for ventilation; if not substantially without such openings, it is of no value. Openings in part of the area will disqualify the entire area; if there are few openings, it may be economical to install fire shutters in them to obtain the protective value of the plaster ceiling.

A comparison was made between an effective plaster ceiling and a panel glass-fiber ceiling (the latter just does not exist, so far as the rating bureau is concerned). Using 20 percent as expected return on investment, the original saving in construction cost more than offsets added insurance cost.

Protection of steel columns is probably not justified on the basis of insurance rates alone, but if columns are to be plastered for appearance, it is economical to fireproof them. This means that the detail of covering used must be one which complies with the minimum requirements of the rating bureau (it is not difficult to exceed their requirements), and the protection should go up to the bottom of the beam above. If plans do not clearly specify otherwise, the plasterer may stop the coating just above the line of a suspended ceiling, leaving several feet of column unprotected. Also, it is necessary that *all* columns be protected; if a warehouse or utility area is included in the same building, these columns must get the same treatment to qualify for a lower insurance rate.

Walls which could serve as division walls should be checked carefully for compliance with requirements. There must be no small openings, such as between joists or for ventilation. Fire doors must be properly installed, with concrete block, if used, filled around the openings. Metal-covered fire doors must have a small opening cut through the metal to allow gases from the wood core to escape when heated—this is seldom done at the factory.

Since a high percentage of windows in exterior walls may raise the rate, addition of windows not only may be an increased initial cost but may cause an increase in insurance cost as well.

Provision of a specified number of fire extinguishers may reduce the rate sufficiently to repay the cost, depending on the factors previously mentioned, such as original/annual cost ratio and valuation per square foot of floor space. In one instance, such an installation was found to be economical in a department store, with an original/annual cost ratio of 5:1.

Application

A designer who repeats the same type of construction for the same type of owner (in terms of original/annual cost ratio) can afford to investigate the type of construction he is using and to determine the most economical construction from a fire insurance-cost standpoint. On single jobs, this is possible only for major substitutions, such as determining the type of ceiling or type of roof construction on the entire project. It is important that the designer study the actual rating sheet for the building, and become familiar with the method of rating, in order intelligently to choose the construction methods to be used.

Mechanical Installations

Recent trends toward a basic structure of low cost and increased facilities for air conditioning and lighting result in a higher proportion of construction cost due to mechanical installations. Mechanical and electrical work may cost from 20 to 50 percent, or more, of the total cost of building, depending on the type of construction; the proportion of annual cost of mechanical installations is even greater.

Air-conditioning equipment is becoming less costly but has lower efficiency and shorter operating life. Because of this trend, and because of the trend toward more and better equipment of all types, the annual cost of such equipment is an important item of overall cost.

Obsolescence

Mechanical equipment is often discarded and replaced while still adequate for its original purpose; commercial buildings in particular often require major alterations, or are used for different purposes, a few years after construction. In this way, mechanical equipment may be abandoned.

In selecting equipment, the possibility of such future changes must be considered; any anticipated major revision will make obsolescence a major item of estimated cost. Selection of proposed systems may depend on the cost of revision of them for accommodation of changes.

Maintenance

The maintenance cost depends both on the actual cost required and the maintenance policy of the owner. For example, compare two similar office air-conditioning systems, one in the office of a large industrial plant and one in a commercial office building.

The industrial plant owner can be expected to establish an elaborate maintenance schedule for air-conditioning equipment, in line with the plant equipment maintenance, possibly involving regular inspection several times a day as well as weekly or monthly lubrication and adjustment operations. The commercial building owner is more likely to just let the equipment run until someone complains he is too hot, and then call a servicing contractor.

The maintenance cost will be higher in the industrial plant, and the equipment may not last any longer. The elaborate maintenance program of the plant may not be justified, but if it is to be maintained anyway, less expensive equipment can be used. The engineer should specify equipment adapted to the maintenance organization, if there is a saving to be had.

Provision for ease of maintenance of mechanical equipment requires cost studies; it is all too common to consume extra building space and to spend money unnecessarily by providing ladders, catwalks, access panels, platforms, and walkways which are rarely used. On the other hand, if space or an access panel is not provided to allow retubing a heat exchanger, for example, the estimated annual cost should include the cost of removing an entire exchanger or the necessary cutting and patching for retubing.

Selection of Equipment

The choice of equipment may be between an inexpensive throwaway unit and an expensive unit with lower maintenance costs and simple replacement of parts. The decision to use the throwaway or the serviceable unit may depend on the available maintenance force, or the size of the force to be used may depend on the type of equipment selected. The throwaway unit requires a relatively unskilled maintenance man, or on-call service by a maintenance contractor.

Since the trend of equipment design is rapidly toward the inexpensive throwaway unit, an increasing premium is being paid to obtain serviceable units. Since, in some lines, it is no longer possible to obtain units which meet former specifications for ease of maintenance, specifications requiring them are not reasonable.

Under some conditions, equipment units will be replaced frequently, even in comparison with other parts of the same system. For example, finned heat-exchange surfaces now have fin spacings as close as fourteen per in. with 0.008-in. aluminum fins, on copper tubing as thin as 0.015

in. If the atmosphere is corrosive, dirt loadings high, or other conditions are adverse, the equipment may be useless in a few years. The original cost of such a standard unit is low enough in comparison to special units that its regular replacement is justified, particularly for higher original/annual cost ratios.

Probability of Failure

An architect or engineer is loath to design work which may be inadequate, even though the savings on the equipment will more than offset the rate occasion of failure. A designer is remembered too often by his work which was unsatisfactory rather than by the fact that the cost of the project was low. It is to be expected, therefore, that an experienced owner who expects an occasional failure can obtain a design of lesser overall cost than can an owner who is inexperienced in the relative cost of avoiding failure.

On two Midwest shopping centers, for example, the consulting engineer would consider only activated-sludge sewage-treatment plants, similar to municipal plants. The owner's own engineer designed and built septic tanks with sand filters which were adequate, at a cost of less than half the consultant's design. The consultant, however, did not want the septic tank to appear as an example of his work, and in addition, it was quite possible that the septic tank would have been inadequate. In such a case, the more expensive system would have had to be installed anyway. The septic-tank design would have been more economical, however, even if the septic tank had been inadequate in a third of the installation in which it was used, that is, if it had but a 67 percent chance of success.

Drainage systems for large parking lots are usually designed by arbitrary, usually unnecessarily conservative standards which do not take local conditions and conditions of occupancy into account. For example, capacity of systems may vary from 2 to 4 in. of rainfall per hour. The latter figure is used to provide the same degree of protection desired for streets, but parking lots do not have the same amount of traffic nor such essential traffic as do streets. Portions may be allowed to flood occasionally, particularly those areas where there is no pedestrian traffic or which are set aside for employee parking.

For example, how much water can be tolerated, and how often, on the least used portion of the parking lot? Such an area may be used but six hours a day for thirty days a year—the peak periods—for a total of one-fiftieth of the time. If we are willing to allow a little water in the low spots once in ten years, then the design rainfall would be that which would occur every 10/50 or 0.2 years. A rainfall that occurred each six months would have one chance in fifty of occurring at a time which would be damaging to that particular area. Different portions of the lot may have differing requirements, since the occupancy rate will vary. If there is ample fall for the drainage system, this saving would not be important.

But if there is very little fall in a parking-lot drainage system, or when rock excavation is required, use of water-surface pipe design, rather than assumption of pipe running full, offers savings. On all but very short lines, pipes are designed to run full of water, so the water surface will be at the top of the pipe. By assuming the water may be allowed to back up to the surface of the ground, additional fall is obtained, which will reduce the required slope or size of the pipe. At the highest pipe elevation, the pipe need be placed only as deep as is necessary to avoid traffic damage, and it may be level for some distance; this saving of several inches raises the entire drainage system a like amount. If the pipe is designed to be under pressure, it may be laid at any convenient slope, including level. Except for the accumulation of water during dry periods, such pipes could be laid uphill, as occurs in an inverted siphon.

Millions of dollars have been unnecessarily spent to avoid something that might happen, when the condition could be corrected when and if it did happen. Examples are insulation of air-conditioning ducts over hung ceilings and in equipment rooms, stainless-steel ducts for corrosive exhausts when aluminum would have been adequate, insulation of water lines to prevent condensation (particularly in air-conditioned spaces), and insulation of outdoor water lines to prevent freezing in mild climates. In northern Ohio the ground may be frozen in winter as deep as 4 ft, but an 8-in. water line placed 8 in. under pavement has given satisfactory service. In this instance, the choice was whether or not to remove a main which had been installed at this depth in error.

On a large air-conditioning project, a saving of $100,000 was made by omitting insulation on discharge ducts, except in inaccessible locations, assuming they could be readily insulated later if condensation should occur. In a location where the outdoor temperature seldom falls below 20°F, several hundred thousand dollars were cut from the cost of an industrial plant by omitting freezing protection. Subsequently, annual costs of repairs, wasted water, and extra labor during cold weather proved to be 10 percent of the amount saved. In this instance, the omission of insulation was justified, since the original/annual cost ratio was 4:1. As might be expected, the maintenance staff was very dissatisfied with the design.

Annual Cost of Air Conditioning

The greater part of annual air-conditioning cost is usually due to the original construction cost; cost of power, water, and maintenance is small in comparison. The first cost of air conditioning is in the range of $400 to $1,200 per ton; thus with an average original/annual cost ratio of 5:1, the annual cost from investment will be in the range of $80 to $240 per ton.

It is common for annual power and water cost to run as low as $20 to $30 per ton, and annual maintenance cost for a small commercial installation will average about $6 to $10 per ton per year.

When high-efficiency air filtration is required, consideration should be given to the new high-efficiency dry-type filters, rather than the better-known electrical precipitating filter. The installed cost of an electrical precipitating filter will be about $500 plus $150 per 1,000 cfm of air capacity, but the dry-type filter can be installed for as little as $40 per 1,000 cfm. The annual operating costs for the electrical-type filters seldom exceed $5 to $10 per 1,000 cfm, as compared with $20 to $40 for the dry type. From this comparison, the added initial cost can be justified only when the original/annual cost ratio is 5:1 or higher.

Fuel

For large boiler installations, consideration should be given to provisions for use of alternate fuels. These provisions allow changes in the fuel source as the market changes and provide an improved bargaining position for the fuel or power purchaser. A design using alternate fuels is more likely to be economical for buildings designed for relatively long life and for a high original/annual cost ratio, such as for public buildings, particularly schools. It is not necessary for these purposes actually to install storage, burners, and other alternative equipment, but it is necessary to provide space and construction for them.

The current effort of utility companies to contact owners directly with biased reports of the efficiency of their products requires the architect or engineer to make a study of the total heating costs for each particular building or type of building.

Even at unusually low electric rates, the relative cost per heat unit is at least twice as great for electricity as for fossil fuels. The utilization efficiency of fuel oil seldom exceeds 70 percent, and 50 percent is not unusual, compared with 100 percent for electricity. The electrical heating system may be less expensive initially, and the operating cost may be less as well, but these circumstances rarely occur.

Let us consider a case where electrical heat proved to be economical—a two-story windowless department store. Insulation in such a building may be "perfect" in the sense that fuel cost is not reduced by added insulation (in fact, fuel costs may be increased by added insulation).

This comes about because the lighting load is sufficient to heat the building; in fact, air conditioning may be required when the outside air temperature is in the 30s at design occupancy of the building. At these temperatures, therefore, a reduction in insulation will help to cool the building, reducing the air-conditioning load. An increase in outside-air intake, of course, would do the same. At lower temperatures, heat loss consists of loss through building walls and loss in exhausted ventilating air; the large proportion of salesroom space requires large volumes of ventilating air and therefore requires large quantities of waste heat; thus most of the heat loss is even then independent of the amount of insulation. In such a building, separate heaters are required in many locations because there is no correlation between heat requirements and ventilation requirements; salesroom spaces require air, and other spaces require heat. This can readily be obtained by electric heaters at less expense than by steam piping. Consequently, there is a considerable saving in initial cost which is not fully compensated for by added fuel cost.

The Heat Pump

Under ideal conditions, a heat pump can produce heat from electricity with a 5:1 ratio; this would indicate that the power cost would be less than the cost of fossil fuels, even at normal rates. However, heat pumps with air sources of heat cannot operate at this efficiency at lower outdoor temperatures, when the greatest amount of heat is required. To compare the operating cost of a heat pump with other heat sources, a seasonal coefficient of performance must be determined—and this coefficient is not always available.

The efficiency of heat pumps can be improved by the use of well water, at greater cost. Even if lower fuel cost is obtained, it would be very unusual for the original cost to be lower than for competitive units, except for one-piece residential units in subtropical locations. Maintenance costs are greater also, and equipment life is shorter than for conventional heating units.

Heating by Lighting

Large multistory buildings with high lighting levels require cooling of the interior areas, even at lowest outdoor temperatures. The excess heat produced in interior areas can be utilized for heating of perimeter areas; buildings have been successfully operated on this basis, even in the northern United States and Canada. For successful operation, the building perimeter must be designed for minimum heat loss (extra insulation, minimum fenestration, and double glazing); the lights must be operated continuously in cold weather, and relatively expensive heat pumps are required for transferring heat from interior to exterior locations. This sort of system would be justified only for a very large building, planned for long life and with low interest rates and favorable electric-power rates. In all-electric-heat installations, the possibility of a subsidy payment from the power company should be investigated.

Total Power

Gas utility companies propose that gas-driven generators produce the electric power for a building as well as heat it, which the companies call the "total power" concept. A number of public schools have been built with this system, the choice being influenced by their high original/annual cost ratio and high cost of power in the area.

Fuel is saved with this arrangement because waste heat from the engine, both from the exhaust and from the cooler system, is utilized for either heating or cooling. Maintenance costs are high, standby equipment is often required to assure a continuous power supply, and equipment life must be considered relatively short.

Annual Power Cost

A number of recent improvements may lower the cost of lighting. Lower power rates can often be obtained by purchase of power at high voltage, but at the cost of greater investment in transformers and related structure. There is also always a possibility that increase in power requirements may make the installation inadequate.

Peak-demand charges for electric power can be substantial; the operation of a 600-hp refrigeration compressor for only thirty-one minutes during a normally cool month can add over $300 per month to the power bill. Since most commercial buildings will require occasional cooling even during the winter months, this is an important factor in design. This added cost may be avoided, but at increased original cost, by installing multiple refrigeration compressors, including at least one small one for such loads. This is another argument for a 100 percent outside-air intake for cooling, minimizing the necessity for refrigeration operation during the winter months.

Increasing demands for higher lighting levels require increased consideration of alternate lighting systems. Incandescent lighting operates with less efficiency than does fluorescent and therefore with higher power cost, but the annual cost of incandescent lighting, due to lower original cost, can still prove to be lower in some cases. The use of incandescent lamps in low-usage areas, such as those for storage and maintenance, will normally be economical.

Relamping of fluorescent fixtures is necessary less often than for incandescents, but the lamp cost is higher, and accessibility is an important consideration in labor cost. Cost of replacement of lamps, including both materials and labor, may be obtained from contractors who specialize in this service. In cases where replacement is difficult, such as high lamps in industrial areas and on outdoor poles, the higher cost of quartz-iodine lamps may be justified by their longer life.

An example of the necessity for cost analysis is illustrated by floodlighting of sports arenas, where the lower cost of incandescent lamps is justified in spite of high operating cost and difficulty of lamp replacement. For this application, lower annual cost is obtained by operating the lamps at higher than rated voltage, obtaining higher efficiency at the expense of operating life. This situation is due to the very short operating hours of the installation. However, a recently developed ceramic arc tube vapor discharge lamp of very high efficiency (over 100 lumens per watt, or about one-third higher than most fluorescents) may be more economical than either of the older types of lamps.

Cost of Increased Light Levels

High lighting levels currently recommended require more than a corresponding increase in cost, and the actual level required should not be exceeded. High lighting levels usually demand year-round air conditioning for all interior areas, which limits air-conditioning design to systems which can offer year-round cooling. This drastically increases both original and annual cost.

For example, increasing the light load by 3 watts per sq ft of floor area (which can be consumed by an increase in the lighting level of 20 to 40 footcandles) requires additional air conditioning, and the total annual cost may be:

Increase in original air-conditioning cost, at $1 per sq ft, or an annual cost of $.20 per sq ft

Annual operating cost of added air conditioning $.15 per sq ft

Increase in original cost of electrical work for added lighting, as annual cost $.30 per sq ft

Additional annual operating cost, for added lighting, $.25 per sq ft
Total annual cost $.90 per sq ft

This is a substantial proportion of the added rents to be obtained
from such buildings, and lease negotiations should take into account
the costs assumed by each party. Many landlords specify that virtually
all of these costs be borne by tenants.

When estimating annual power costs of lighting, it should be anticipated that lighting will be used outside the normal operating hours
of the building occupants. Cleaning and maintenance workers use an
unnecessary amount of lighting, usually outside of normal working hours,
and building occupants will rarely turn off lights even when their use
is not required.

The use of high-frequency ballasts can provide savings in cost of
large fluorescent-light installations; however, the added cost of providing
high-frequency power may be less than the savings in costs of ballasts.
The high-frequency ballast is far less expensive and consumes less current, and there is an absence of stroboscopic effect. Annual costs are
reduced because of lower replacement costs of ballasts, as well as lower
power costs.

Combined Trade Changes

The foregoing examples have emphasized those choices in design
which affect primarily one trade or even one item. Most savings are
made as a result of much more complex changes, and the cost savings
by such changes are difficult to determine. For example, let us consider
the factors involved in the substitution of 3-in. fiber deck for 2-in. deck
in a retail store with steel-joist roof structure.

Ignoring minor items, such as possible increases in parapet height,
edge blocking, and dripstrip width, principal items of cost are:

1. *Cost of Roof-deck Material* This difference will vary with different
manufacturers, and a previously low supplier may not be able to furnish
the new thickness.

2. *Installation of Deck* To the architect, cost is usually the contractor's estimate; the comparable cost of two operations (installation of
light versus heavy decking), involving a 50 percent increase in material
but no increase in the number of pieces or number of fasteners, will
vary from 1:1 to 1:1.5, depending on the method of estimating used
by the contractor.

3. *Steel Joists* The increased weight may require a heavier joist, but
an increased joist spacing, with reduction in the number of members,
will usually result in lower cost. The heavier joist may be a more readily

available item and therefore lower in price because of increased competition. If the 2-in. design required T-bar purlins, their elimination would reduce costs.

4. *Joist Erection* Fewer joists should be less expensive to erect, but this is not always true. The heavier joist may require more men or a crane not previously necessary and therefore may result in higher cost.

5. *Attachment of Hung Ceiling to Joists* The number of wires supporting ceiling runners depends both on the minimum spacing of wires on the runner and on the spacing of joists. The change may result in either more or fewer wires. If 24- by 48-in. lay-in panels are being used, a change in joist spacing may require a change in direction of main members, with resulting cost changes.

6. *Hearing and Air Conditioning* Required capacity will be decreased, which reduces both original and annual cost, but as previously pointed out, under some conditions of lighting, the insulation change is not important.

7. *Duct Insulation* With an increase in roof insulation in comparison with ceiling insulation, the cost of air-conditioning the space between roof and ceiling may be reduced. This may make the omission of duct insulation permissible, with consequent savings.

It is difficult to obtain true costs of changes of this type, since the subcontractors themselves may not know what the labor-cost differences are. Major items can be determined by alternates on bids, but it is a burden on the general contractor to require alternates whenever a choice is to be made. If alternates are bid once for each kind of construction, these results can be used in design for a considerable period with some confidence that the economical construction is being installed. It is suggested that such information should be made available to all architects in each area, through local AIA chapters or state organizations. The usual publicized information of this type lacks sufficient detail to be useful.

Choosing methods of construction which will result in the lowest cost to the owner requires information on what the owner considers his annual cost because of added investment to be, as well as information on his maintenance program and policies. For one owner these do not vary greatly, but the economical construction of a building type will be different, depending on the owner's capital position and the risk involved. This capital cost is not necessarily the interest cost on a loan, unless there is additional money available at the same rate to pay for added work. Even if the mortgage more than covers the entire cost of the project, use of the interest rate as annual cost is unrealistic; the owner may be able to use the surplus cash to provide a higher return than the interest rate he pays. On this basis, public buildings normally justify a higher investment to avoid depreciation than does private construction. The original/annual cost ratio also depends on income-tax planning.

When available, an owner's maintenance superintendent can provide valuable suggestions, although it is necessary to analyze added construction carefully; apparently badly needed work may not actually be profitable. On the other hand, some low-cost construction items are also low-maintenance items.

The computation of fire insurance rates for the building should be reviewed by the architect to correct any construction deficiencies.

The types of heating and air-conditioning systems and lighting also depend on this original/annual cost ratio. It may be profitable to install work of doubtful sufficiency, if savings warrant. From the architect's viewpoint, this may be accomplished only if the owner fully understands the risk and is ready to accept the consequences.

It is not the intent of this chapter to urge more or less expensive construction. It is well known that some designs are unnecessarily expensive and that others lack features which would reduce annual cost at comparatively low original cost. In each case, a study of the total annual cost for alternatives should be made, and it is not to be expected that the results of the study will be the same for different circumstances.

FOUR

Justin Sweet

Legal Aspects
of Building Costs

Architects often must resort to litigation to collect for their services when projects are abandoned because of a great variation between low construction bids and the amount clients expected to pay. Architects should have a basic understanding of the legal doctrines which govern their rights and duties if this situation arises. This legal analysis will focus upon those aspects of the problem that have caused the greatest difficulty. Spotlighting these problems, coupled with techniques for avoiding them, can materially reduce the likelihood of future difficulties.

First, some general observations on the legal analysis. Despite the frequent use of form contracts, architects and clients still make varying types of contractual arrangements. This dilutes the precedent value of court decisions. Slight differences in the wording of contracts often change the legal result.

Legal rules and their application vary from state to state. Even within a state the results will vary, depending upon the judge, the jury, and the particular facts in the case. An attorney can be invaluable, both in preventing difficulties and in rendering legal advice if disputes do arise.

Not every conclusion drawn in the analysis is supported by a precise case precedent. Many of the points discussed have not been decided by the courts. My conclusions on these questions are based upon general principles of contract law, the reasonable expectations of the architect and client, and the realities of architectural practice.

Promises and Conditions—Due Care and Accuracy

If the lowest construction bid substantially exceeds the amount the client expected to pay, architect and client sometimes disagree over their respective rights and duties. Difficulties can develop over the following questions:

1. If the project is given up, does the client have to pay for architectural services provided before abandonment?

2. Has the architect fulfilled his contractual obligations to the client?

The answer to these questions involves a comparison of promises and conditions.

A *promise* is an assurance given by the promisor to the promisee that a certain performance will be rendered or that a certain event will occur. Usually the failure of the performance to be made, or the event to occur, will mean the promisor has breached and may be liable for damages. In the context of architect-client contracts, an architect may promise the client that the contractors' bids will be within a cost figure set by the client. If this event—the bids being within the figure— does not occur, the architect may be liable for any damages suffered by the client because of delay or rising costs during redesign.

A *condition* is an event, which can include a promised performance, which must occur or be excused before another promised performance or event becomes due. As an example, to obtain a commission, the architect might agree to risk his fee on the accuracy of his cost estimates. If so, a condition has been established concerning the client's obligation to pay. First the contractors' bids must be received, showing the accuracy of the architect's estimates. Only then, under the agreement as stated above, would the client have a duty to pay the architect's fee.

Cost problems usually involve a determination of the exact nature of the architect's promise with regard to costs and of the exact nature of the event which must occur, or be excused, before the client is obligated to pay a fee.

The exact nature of the architect's promise first depends on what assurance he has given the client, orally or in writing. Next, it will depend on the nature of the promises that are *implied*, rather than expressed. Implied promises depend upon the surrounding circumstances, custom, and the law. The architect might be held to have promised:

1. To use due care
2. To be accurate
3. That the project cost would not exceed a particular amount

If the architect, unwisely, has *promised* to be accurate, normally the reason for inaccuracy is not relevant. In effect, he has guaranteed the accuracy of his estimate. If he is not correct, he has breached and is liable for any resulting damages suffered by the client.

The exact nature of the event that *conditions* the client's obligation to pay the fee depends upon the agreement, surrounding facts and circumstances, and the application of the legal doctrine of conditions. The event might be:

1. Use of due care in preparing architectural cost estimates
2. The project cost not exceeding a specified amount or the final cost estimate
3. The client being satisfied with the bids (or bidders)
4. The availability of adequate funds
5. The project being built

Failure of these events to occur or be excused would mean the client need not pay the fee.

A promise can be, and often is, a condition. The architect could be held to have promised to use due care, and the exercise of due care could also condition the client's obligation to pay the fee. The architect might, unwisely, promise to be accurate, as well as condition his right to a fee upon the accuracy of his cost estimate. In such a case, the architect would not be entitled to collect his fee, and could also be held for damages for breach of contract.

The promise and the condition need not be identical. The architect might promise only to use due care, and yet, by agreement, his fee could be conditioned upon the accuracy of his estimate, the bids being acceptable, or the project being built. In the case of accuracy, if he used due care but was inaccurate, he could not recover his fee but would not be liable for damages for breach of contract.

Definitions

The term *cost condition,* as used in this chapter, will mean an arrangement under which the parties agree that the client's obligation to pay a fee is conditioned upon the project being possible of accomplishment within a specified cost amount, without regard to whether or not the architect exercised due care. Since, in the normal case, the architect has given a cost estimate which is within the specified amount, for all practical purposes this condition is synonymous with accurate cost predictions. Failure of the condition to occur or be excused will relieve the client from having to pay a fee, and might result in the client's recovery of interim fee payments.

Architects use a number of related, but somewhat differing, terms in discussing costs. One of the reasons for disputes over cost stems from the failure of architects to use terms which have a consistent meaning within the profession and which give the client a clear understanding of the agreement concerning the effect of inaccurate cost predictions.

A *cost budget* is a figure supplied by the client, and concurred in by the architect, at the commencement of the architect-client relationship, or at various other times during the existence of the relationship. This budget represents the approximate amount which the client wishes to spend for the project. Use of a budget usually means that quantity and quality are more important to the client than costs, although there are always limits to budget flexibility.

Cost estimates are made by the architect at periodic intervals during his performance. The estimates represent the architect's best considered judgment of what the project will ultimately cost. The estimates should become progressively more accurate as details of the project are worked out. Prior to 1961, the AIA standard contract specified that cost estimates would be supplied by the architect, if requested by the owner. Since 1961, the AIA contract has required the architect to give "statements of probable project construction costs" at each phase of the architect's performance.

A *fixed cost limitation* is a sum specified by the client and concurred in by the architect, intended to fix a maximum limit on construction costs. If the project cannot be accomplished within this amount, the client retains the right to abandon the project. In public contracts, frequently this figure is the amount of money appropriated for the project. Fixed cost limitations are more rigid than cost budgets. Use of a fixed cost limitation means the client is more concerned with costs than with quantity or quality, although there are obvious limits to quantity and quality flexibility. If the architect agrees to a fixed cost limitation, he should be most conscious of costs during his performance. The creation of a fixed-cost limitation should mean that the client will cede decisions on certain minor quality and quantity details to the architect.

Cost ceiling and cost range are sometimes used. A *cost ceiling* has the same meaning as a fixed cost limitation. A *cost range* means a cost budget with a high and low figure rather than a single amount.

The creation of a fixed cost limitation does not necessarily mean that a cost condition has been created. It is possible for the client to set a firm limit on costs without conditioning his obligation to pay a fee upon the project being brought in within that amount. This is the objective of the present standard-form AIA contract.

Creation of a Cost Condition

In the typical dispute over excessive costs, client and architect usually agree that costs were discussed both before and during the architect's performance. Usually both parties agree upon the amount of the projected cost. They may even agree that the cost figure was "firm," or that a fixed cost limitation was created. The focus of disputes concerns the architect's right to be paid when the project is given up because the objectives of the client could not be attained within the specified cost figure. The client states that he had been assured that, if the project could not be brought in within the specified amount, he would not be obligated to pay the architect's fees. The architect usually denies any agreement to that effect and points to the absence of such a provision from the writing, or even to a written disclaimer which he claims negates any such understanding. The two principal legal issues relevant to the resolution of the question of whether a cost condition has been created are:

1. Does the execution of a written agreement not containing a cost condition preclude the client from testifying about the asserted agreement?

2. What factors are relevant in the determination of whether such an agreement took place?

One preliminary question sometimes raised by architects will not be discussed in detail in this chapter. This relates to the professional propriety of making a contract under which the architect stakes his fee upon the accuracy of his cost estimates. Such agreements are made, and are often even required, in public contracts. Courts have enforced such agreements, denying the architect recovery of his fee when they have found that such agreements have been made. This has been done despite the traditional reluctance of the courts to permit a forfeiture.

A *forfeiture* results when a person renders services, or furnishes goods. and is denied payment by the law. If the court determines that clear evidence supports the conclusion that this risk was assumed by one of the parties to the contract, it will enforce the forfeiture. Whatever relief the party can obtain must come from application of the legal concept known as *quasi contract*. This concept is not based upon contract, but upon the principle of unjust enrichment. Quasi-contractual recovery requires a benefit conferred upon the client. If the plans are not used, generally no benefit has been conferred upon the client. For this reason, quasi contract has been of little value to the architect.

Most of the cost-condition cases have involved the issue of whether the client will be permitted to testify about the asserted oral agreement relieving the client from obligation to pay if the project could not be brought within a specified cost-condition figure. The court's resolution of this issue has involved the *parol evidence rule*.

The parol evidence rule is complex in background and confused in application. Stated briefly, the law has had great difficulty in deciding whether to admit evidence of alleged antecedent or contemporaneous oral agreements which are not contained in a *subsequently* executed writing. The parol evidence rule does not apply to bar evidence of oral agreements made after the execution of a written agreement.

Historically, the rationale for the rule has been stated to be a reflection of the court's doubts as to whether a particular oral agreement took place and a reluctance to submit this question to lay juries. Creation of the parol evidence rule permitted the judges to exclude evidence of such prior, oral agreements, avoiding consideration of the difficult question of credibility, and removing the issue of credibility from the jury. Later, some courts justified retention of the rule by stating that the desired stability in commercial transactions could come only by denying enforcement of asserted prior oral agreements. Other courts believed that denial of enforcement of prior oral agreements would induce parties to put their entire agreement in writing.

Today, some courts phrase the rule as one which rejects evidence of prior oral agreements because such evidence would "vary, add to, or contradict" a subsequent written agreement. Other courts articulate the rule as one which deals with the presumptive completeness of writings. Still other courts speak of the necessity of using all available evidence to determine whether the parties intended to integrate their entire agreement in one final and complete writing. These variant approaches have caused confusion and have made the application of the rule most uncertain.

It should be noted that the parol evidence rule deals only with the question of whether the party will be *permitted* to testify about the alleged agreement. Even if the client is permitted to testify, the architect will be given the opportunity of telling his side of the story. If admitted, the ultimate determination of the existence of such an oral agreement, and its effect, will be made by the judge or the jury. Attorneys for architects vigorously contest the admissibility question, evidently feeling that if the evidence is admitted, it will be believed by the fact finder.

Prediction concerning the admissibility of testimony about an alleged prior or contemporaneous oral agreement on costs is hazardous, because of the differing attitudes toward the rule from state to state, and even within a given state. Nevertheless, certain generalizations can be extrapolated from a reading of the many decisions which have involved architect-client contracts.

If the agreement is silent on the question of costs or fixed cost limitations, it is likely that the client will be permitted to testify on the alleged agreement. There have been a few cases to the contrary, usually where the contract has mentioned cost estimates in some way. However, most courts assume that costs are discussed in every case. If no mention is made of any understanding on costs, these courts assume that the writing is not complete.

Prediction on admissibility of evidence of prior oral agreements relating to costs is more difficult if there is language in the writing which deals in one way or another with this question. Prior to 1961, the standard AIA contract merely stated that the architect did not guarantee estimates. A number of cases have interpreted this clause, and the results illustrate the difficulty of predicting the success of this disclaimer, as well as disclaimers generally.

A case before the Wisconsin Supreme Court in 1944 involved a written contract executed *after* the completion and approval of preliminaries. The court held that the trial court had committed error when it permitted the client to testify about an understanding on excessive costs. The court stressed that when the contract was signed, a good deal of the detail had been worked out. The court held the written contract to be completed.

An Illinois decision in 1954 involved the identical clause. This case is distinguished from the Wisconsin case on the basis of when the contract was executed. In the Illinois case, the contract was signed *before* there had been any agreement on details and before the architect had started his work. The court also emphasized that the client had not read the agreement and that it had been pulled from the architect's drawer with a casual remark by the architect that the agreement merely precluded the client from changing architects.

In a later case, the Texas Court of Civil Appeals attempted to reconcile the two earlier decisions. The court held that a writing executed *after* preliminaries are approved is complete, since the client can no longer make major changes. Since the writing was complete, evidence of an alleged, oral agreement would not be received by the court.

From the standpoint of the architect, a synthesis of these cases is not very encouraging. The architect normally wants, and is encouraged, to obtain a written agreement with the client as soon as possible. If this is done, the pre-1961 disclaimer will not be of much use in avoiding testimony by the client about an alleged prior oral agreement on costs.

The 1961 AIA contract (and later editions of it) is a vast improvement. It recognizes the possibility of a fixed cost limitation, sets up a method for hiring cost estimators if a limitation is created, provides for the handling of situations where the bids are too high, substitutes "statements of probable project construction costs" for estimates, and although somewhat indirectly, deals with the question of fee through the abandonment clause. It is reasonably well drafted, and will certainly do better in the courts than did its predecessor, even though subjected to a test of completeness based upon when it is executed.

Nevertheless, there is always a risk that, when the client's expectations differ from the contract, the courts will interpret the clause narrowly. Even well-drawn clauses can be attacked by assertion of fraud or mistake, by a request that the writing be *reformed* because it did not correctly express the true understanding of the parties, or by a claim that the agreement was made after formation of the contract and thus not affected by the parol evidence rule. The client could convince the judge that he is using the oral agreement only to interpret the writing, if the contract does not *explicitly* state that the client need not pay if the costs are too high. No contractual provision, however well drawn, will ensure that the client will not be able to bring his contention before the judge and jury. No clause, however well-drafted, can displace the need for a thorough exploration with the client over the cost question, along with a clear, comprehensive provision which expresses the common understanding of the parties on the effect of excessive costs on the client's obligation to pay the architect his fee.

The courts have looked at factors other than the written or asserted oral agreement in resolving the question of the creation of the cost condition. Even if the client's testimony is received into evidence, the question of determining whether the agreement did take place as alleged must be resolved by the court or jury.

Courts have admitted evidence of custom in the profession. Architects have been permitted to introduce evidence that customarily architects do not assume the risk of the accuracy of their cost predictions. Also, courts have been more favorably disposed toward holding for the architect if the project in question has involved remodeling rather than new construction, since estimating costs in remodeling is extremely difficult. The same result should follow if the type of construction involves experimental techniques or materials.

Decisions by the courts sometimes turn on the amount of detail given to the architect by the client in advance. Generally, the greater the detail, the easier it should be for the architect to predict accurately. However, it is much more difficult for the architect to achieve the desires of the client within a specified cost figure if the client retains a great deal of control over details, especially if these controls are exercised throughout the architect's performance. For this reason, some courts have held that a cost condition is not created where the architect is not given much flexibility in designs or materials.

Some courts have looked at the stage of the architect's performance in which the cost condition was created. If it is created at an early stage, it is more difficult for the architect to be accurate in his cost predictions. If it is imposed later, creation—or, more realistically, imposition—may be an unfair attempt by the client to deprive the architect of his fee. Generally, the earlier the cost limit is imposed, the less likely it is to be a cost condition.

Occasionally the courts have applied the rule that an ambiguous contract should be interpreted against the person who drew it up and thus created the ambiguity. If the client is a private party, the contract is usually drafted or supplied by the architect.

Courts have looked at the building and business experience of the client. If the client is experienced, he should be more aware of the difficulty of making accurate cost estimates. If he has building experience, the client is more likely to be aware of the custom that architects usually do not risk their fee upon the accuracy of their cost estimates.

Courts have sometimes cited provisions for interim payments as an indication that the architect is not assuming the risk of the accuracy of his cost estimates. However, standard printed clauses buried in a contract are not always an accurate reflection of the understanding of the party not familiar with the customs or the forms. If payments have been *made* during the architect's performance, this is a clearer indication that the client is not laboring under the belief that he will not have to pay any fee if the low bid substantially exceeds the final cost estimate.

A few cases have looked for good faith on the part of the client. For example, if the client has offered some payment to the architect for his services, this may impress a court as a show of fairness and good faith.

On the whole, architects have not fared well in court. Courts often assume that a fixed cost limitation means a cost condition. Such decisions do not draw a line between permission for the client to terminate the arrangement if costs are too high and agreements under which the architect would go uncompensated for services which may prove to have little or no value to the client.

Courts have failed to recognize the professional nature of the architect-client relationship. The architect renders professional services and gives professional advice. He is not an entrepreneur, seeking maximum profits and risking financial loss when things do not go right. Courts sometimes use reasoning which is more appropriate to an arm's-length sale of goods, rather than that for a professional relationship where joint participation is directed toward the common objective of finding a professional solution for the client's problem.

Finally, some courts, and many clients, believe that cost estimating is a science and that an architect should be able to crank out reliable estimates routinely.

Avoiding Misunderstanding

As has been emphasized, a conscious effort must be made to arrive at a mutually acceptable understanding on the cost question, and this must be followed by a careful expression of the understanding in the written contract. If, as is usually the case, the architect does not want to create a cost condition, he should show a well-drafted disclaimer clause, such as the present AIA clause, to the client. He should explain the clause, its language, and its rationale. He should stress the difficulty of making accurate cost estimates, especially at early stages of the design. He should explain the process under which costs are predicted, compare his methods with that of the contractor, and should articulate the reasons for the extreme variations in construction bids. He should stress the client's control over details and the frequent need for changes in the solution. If necessary, the architect should offer to redesign if the bids are more than a specified percentage over the cost estimate, while ex-plaining that redesign is very costly to the architect.

If the client is persuaded by the explanation, cost figures should be designated as a cost estimate, budget, or statement of probable construction costs, whichever is appropriate. If a fixed cost limitation is being created without intent to affect the architect's right to the fee, this must be spelled out in the contract. The architect should prepare and retain memos of all conversations with clients over costs. Copies of the memos should be sent to the client for his concurrence, as soon as possible.

Some architects may believe that all this cautionary advice is too cumbersome, too legalistic and, most important, will lose clients. If a reasonable explanation is made in advance, including a promise to redesign, such an explanation should satisfy most clients. A recent empirical study of cost problems showed that 50 percent of the disputes with clients over excessive costs were disposed of by an explanation which satisfied the client. If this percentage can be satisfied *after* a problem develops, an even higher percentage of disputes can be avoided by a sensible explanation in advance of possible misunderstandings.

If the explanation does not convince the client of the fairness of the architect's position, in some cases the architect is well rid of the client. In other cases, an adjustment in the fee may satisfy both parties. There is nothing immoral or unprofessional in using compromise to resolve an honest impasse. It *is* unprofessional not to raise and adjust a problem which so frequently causes disputes and leads to litigation.

Unless the problem is discussed in advance and disposed of to the mutual satisfaction of the parties, the probability of misunderstanding and dispute is high, often resulting in a lost or reduced fee for the architect.

Interpretation

If it is established that a cost condition has been created, the next issue is that of interpretation. What is necessary to satisfy the cost condition?

The architect is permitted some margin of error. Courts have adopted a test which employs a type of substantial performance. Many architects suggest, and many public contracts permit, a deviation of 10 percent.

The cost figure which determines the occurrence of the condition is usually the construction bid submitted by the contractor. Normally cost of acquiring the land, consultants' fees, and fees of the architect are not considered costs for this purpose.

Sometimes *ultimate* costs exceed the low bid because of extra work or because unforeseen circumstances develop in performance which lead to the contractor being given an increase in the contract price. The cost of extra work should not bear upon the cost condition, unless the extra work is needed to compensate for design errors of the architect. An illustration of unforeseen circumstances would be the discovery of unexpected subsoil conditions, which could lead to a price increase. This should have no bearing upon the cost condition.

To sum up, in the normal situation, the condition has occurred if a low, enforceable bid is received which is reasonably close to the cost-condition figure.

Implication of Terms—Redesign

In addition to determining what the parties have expressly agreed to, courts are often called upon to fill in contractual gaps which either were not considered by the parties or were terms which they believed to be so obvious that contractual expression was unnecessary. This filling of contractual gaps by the courts is called *implication of terms*. As a rule, courts are reluctant to imply terms. They will do so if firmly convinced that:

1. Had the question been called to the attention of the parties at the time the contract was made, the parties would have agreed to this interpretation.

2. Or, without implication, the object of one or both of the contracting parties would be drastically frustrated.

3. Or, implication is needed to make a binding contract when the parties intended to be bound.

4. Or, in extreme cases, an implication of terms is demanded by basic notions of equity and good sense.

Implication of terms is important for this chapter in relation to the problems of redesign by the architect and cooperation by the client in reducing costs.

If all the bids are too high, does the architect have a right to redesign in order to meet the cost condition? The first consideration must be that of the contract terms. However, even if there is no contractual provision providing for a right to redesign, the architect should be given this opportunity. The arrangement between architect and client is a professional relationship, where both parties should do their utmost to accomplish the goals of both the client and the architect. Frequently, redesign can avoid forfeiture of the architect's fee.

Cooperation by the client should also be required. The client should not be expected to agree to a material change of the design solution agreed to earlier by architect and client. The client should not have to go farther than agreeing to cheapening of the work. The basic design should continue, but the changes should relate to reducing the cost without affecting the utility and purpose of the project.

The 1961 AIA contract (and later versions) gives the architect a right to redesign, requires the client to cooperate, and, in addition, requires the client to *increase* his cost limit. This is going rather far. It is most unlikely that a court would *imply* this, in addition to the right to redesign and cooperation.

There are limits to the right to redesign. If the delay inherent in redesign would work a material hardship on the client, the architect should not be given the opportunity to redesign. Also, if the variance between the low bid and the cost condition is so extreme that it appears unlikely that redesign will be successful, then the architect should not have the right to redesign.

Should the law imply a promise by the architect that he will redesign if the client so wishes? If a cost condition is created, and the architect does not want to redesign, he should not be required to do so. He has already lost his fee, and it would be unfair to require him to try to bring the project within the cost condition if he does not think it feasible. The implication of such a promise would be a type of compulsion hardly suitable to the architect-client professional relationship.

Even if there is no cost condition, it is unlikely that the law would or should require redesign. Usually, the architect does not *promise* to bring the project in at a specified cost.

Condition Excused

The duty to perform a promise does not arise until events which condition performance either occur or are excused. *Excuse* can be divided into a number of related, but analytically different, concepts. These are prevention, hindrance, lack of cooperation, estoppel, waiver, and impossibility. Judicial decisions have not always respected the analytical distinctions. Courts often use waiver to include almost any type of situation which excuses the condition. However, definition of these concepts should facilitate a better understanding of the basic concept of excuse of conditions.

Prevention, Hindrance, or Lack of Cooperation

If the client unjustifiably prevents the cost condition from occurring, hinders the occurrence of the condition, or fails to take reasonable, positive action which would cause the condition to occur, the condition is excused and the promise matures. The client should not be permitted to set up the failure of the condition to occur as a defense under these circumstances. This doctrine is based on fairness.

A refusal by the client to discuss the project or to furnish necessary information would excuse the cost condition. This would be a clear case of lack of cooperation. The same result would follow if the client refused to discuss the architect's solution or to consider approval of the plans.

Excessive changes ordered by the client during design phases would be prevention, since the architect normally must comply with client-directed changes. However, if the changes were necessary to compensate for design errors or omissions, or if the architect did not inform the client of the effect the changes would have on costs (and the client was not aware of the effect of increased costs due to changes, from some other source of information), then the changes should not excuse the condition.

Prevention can arise during the bidding phase. If the client refuses to submit invitations to any bidders or to attempt to negotiate a contract, the condition would be excused.

The client could prove to be so difficult to deal with during the prebid period, or during the bid negotiations, that he would be unable to find a contractor willing to enter into a contract with him. Some client irascibility may be expected when the architect agrees to work with a particular client, but if the irascibility is motivated solely by a desire to avoid a fee, the cost condition should be excused.

What if the client refuses to use a representative group of bidders? What if the client refuses to permit a particular contractor to bid, or refuses to negotiate with a reputable contractor who is willing to do the work within the cost condition amount? Clearly the condition should be excused in those cases where the client's principal motive is to avoid paying the architect his fee. Even if the client has an honest reason for his refusal, the condition should be excused. The architect should not have to take the risk that only a bid by a contractor satisfactory to the client will satisfy the condition, unless the contract so specifies. The client cannot be compelled to enter into a contract with a builder against his will, but his failure to do so may constitute lack of cooperation and excuse the cost condition.

A low bid may be received within the cost-condition amount, but the bidder may ask to be released from his bid because of an alleged computation error or because of the omission of a key cost item from his bid computation. There is a current trend toward granting relief in such cases. A judicial determination relieving the contractor from his bid would mean that the condition has not occurred. Occurrence of the condition requires a judicially enforceable bid within the cost figure. The condition should not be excused if the release is based upon the honest belief of the client, or on a legal opinion of his attorney, that the bidder would be able to obtain judicial relief. The client should not be compelled to go to court to avoid excusing the cost condition.

What if the client releases the bidder, not because of belief or advice that the bidder could obtain judicial relief, but because of the client's honest belief that it would be inequitable to compel the bidder to stick to his bid or a belief that a dissatisfied bidder will not do a good job? Conceding the honesty and soundness of the client's judgment, the condition should be excused in such a case. The client may release the bidder, but the cost condition has been excused, and the architect is entitled to his fee.

Even if there is prevention, hindrance, or lack of cooperation, the condition is not excused unless the architect can show, with reasonable certainty, that the cost condition would have occurred had it not been prevented or hindered, or had there been cooperation. When courts want to overlook this requirement, they often use waiver. This, as will be seen, does not require a showing that the condition would have occurred. In any case, judicial inquiry into probability of occurrence is likely to be perfunctory if the conduct, or failure to act, by the client seems motivated by bad faith.

Estoppel

Estoppel is a legal concept based upon reliance or change of position. When one party has indicated he does not intend to enforce a provision in his favor and the other party relies upon this and fails to take steps that would make the condition occur, the condition cannot later be asserted as a defense. Estoppel does not require malice or bad faith, but merely justifiable reliance.

In the architect-client context, estoppel would result if the client, either by words or acts, led the architect to believe the cost condition would not be enforced by the client, and the architect failed to take steps which he could have taken to bring the costs within the amount established by the cost condition.

An easy illustration would be the client telling the architect that he was so pleased by the design that he did not care about costs. If the architect then proceeded with the design, when he could have changed the design and caused the condition to occur, the client would be estopped from asserting the condition, and the condition would be excused.

Approval of the preliminaries or construction documents may cause the architect not to make design changes which would have brought the costs within the cost-condition amount. However, estoppel would arise only if the approval were given with knowledge that the cost would exceed the cost-condition figures. Normally, this knowledge would come from a revised cost estimate given by the architect, although the client could become aware of the effect on costs in some other way. Reliance by the architect, without such knowledge on the part of the client, would not be reasonable. If so, there would be no estoppel to prevent the client from asserting the cost condition as a defense to an action by the architect to collect his fee.

What if approval of the plans were accompanied by a statement by the client that he still wanted to stand upon the cost condition, but that he could not take the time to wait for the architect to redesign? If the time pressure is the result of unexcused delays of the architect, the condition should not be excused. If the client proceeds to use the plans, he will have to pay for their use. In such a case, the architect's right to payment would not be based on the contract, since the cost condition has neither occurred nor been excused. Recovery would be based upon the doctrine of quasi contract, which is predicated upon unjust enrichment. (Quasi contract will be covered more fully when the use of plans is discussed.) If the time pressure is not the fault of the architect, and he could have satisfied the condition by redesign, there is detrimental reliance. The cost condition is excused, and the promise to pay the architect's fee enforced.

What if the client is informed of the excessive cost estimate but decides to submit the plans to bid because he believes the architect is too conservative? If the bids are too high, the architect should be given a right to redesign. In addition, any additional costs due to the delay in redesign should be charged to the client. If redesign is no longer feasible, the condition should be excused if redesign earlier could have caused the condition to occur.

Sometimes estoppel is based upon interim fee payments made by the client despite his awareness that the cost would be likely to exceed the cost-condition figure. This knowledge may come from higher cost estimates given by the architect, or from other sources of information. In such a case, the architect may reasonably be led to believe that the client no longer intends to enforce the original cost condition. If the architect has relied on this as reason for not redesigning, the condition will be excused.

Estoppel could also arise if the client used the plans, despite knowledge of the excessive cost. Here, the client's knowledge is usually easy to establish, since the use usually occurs after the bids are in. If the client let the contract rather than permitting the architect to redesign, and if this was due to inadequate time for redesign, the question of estoppel would depend upon the reason for the time pressure. If the fault was that of the architect, it is probable that he has no right to redesign, and the cost condition would not be excused. Recovery in such a case would have to be based on quasi contract or unjust enrichment.

Since quasi contract is based upon unjust enrichment, the measure of recovery will be the benefit conferred on the client by the use of the plans. This might be measured by the reasonable value of the architect's services, a measure not too different from that of the contract remedies available to the architect had there been no cost condition. If the architect did not estimate very accurately, he would be likely to find that a court would hold that the benefit conferred was of a lesser value than what the architect would have received under the contract. Because quasi contract is not a well-developed legal doctrine, courts sometimes use estoppel or waiver loosely in what are essentially quasi-contract cases.

Note that estoppel is not based upon an actual intention on the part of the client to dispense with the cost condition. It is based upon words or acts which lead the architect so to believe, followed by detrimental reliance.

Waiver

Waiver is related to estoppel, but there is an analytical distinction not always drawn by courts. Estoppel is based upon detrimental reliance, upon the concept that, but for the act constituting the estoppel, the architect would have caused the cost condition to occur. To create a waiver, there need be no showing of reliance, or that the condition would have occurred. All that is required is evidence that the client has communicated an intention to pay the fee, despite the failure of the cost condition to occur. The condition was for his benefit. If he manifested an intention to give up this benefit, he should be held to his communicated intention, and the cost condition should be excused. Because of its simplicity, most of the cases have used waiver to excuse the condition. This avoids the need for going into the true elements of estoppel, which, in many cases, would be difficult for the architect to show.

Waiver is relatively easy if the intention is clearly expressed by oral or written communication. For example, if the client states that he is so pleased with the design that he does not care about costs, the condition will be waived without any need to show reliance by the architect. Even if the architect could never have met the cost condition, the waiver is likely to be held to excuse the condition.

The most difficult aspect of this seemingly simple formula for excusing conditions is in determining what acts manifest waiver, other than express statements. Often, waiver is predicated upon acts that have been discussed—approval of plans, excessive changes, payments, or use of plans. Acts such as these can often have ambiguous meanings. Do they manifest an intention on the part of the client to dispense with the condition? An important element in deciding on the legal effect of these acts is awareness by the client, when the acts are performed, that costs are likely to exceed the amount of the cost condition. The architect can hardly assume that these acts manifest the requisite intent of waiver on the part of the client if the client is not aware of the likelihood of excessive costs. For this reason, as well as others, the architect must keep the client constantly informed on current cost estimates—especially after changes made by the client. If he does not, a court is less likely to hold that these acts by the client waive the condition.

If acts such as payment, changes, approval of plans, or use of plans occur, but the client makes it quite clear that he is not giving up the condition, there is no waiver. Estoppel will be difficult to find, because the statement of the client's intention to stand on the condition should make any reliance by not redesigning unjustifiable. In such a case, the condition is still in effect. If the client has used the plans, the recovery should be predicated upon quasi contract.

Impossibility

Architects sometimes assert that performance of the cost condition became impossible because of circumstances over which they have no control.

A condition of a minor or technical nature may be excused if its occurrence became impossible, and if the risk of impossibility has not been assumed by the promisee (in this case, the architect). Without going into the difficult question of whether a cost condition is minor or technical, the creation of a cost condition means the architect assumes the risk of most prediction factors. This includes a steep rise in wage and material costs, or volatility of the construction market, factors which help to make cost prediction difficult. This is one of the primary reasons for avoiding the creation of a cost condition by a clear understanding with the client and by use of an appropriate disclaimer clause in the contract.

A cataclysmic event, such as a war or great natural catastrophe, might cause a different result. If costs become excessive for these reasons, normally use of the plans will constitute a waiver, and the cost condition will be excused. If the plans are not used, the architect will recover if the contract provided that he would be paid if the project was abandoned for any reason. Even without such an "abandonment" clause, the condition should be excused. The architect created the design requested by the client but, because of *extraordinary* reasons beyond his control, not at the price limit set. Creation of a cost condition places most risks upon the architect, but not every conceivable risk.

The doctrine of excuse by impossibility has not been of much assistance to the architect. Where the question of creation of the condition is close, the decision should be resolved for the architect if the reason for the excess cost is related to unforeseeable and catastrophic circumstances.

Measure of Recovery by the Architect

If the court finds that no cost condition was created, or that if one was created, it was excused, what is the measure of the architect's recovery? This discussion assumes that the client does not permit the project to be continued.

Under normal contract principles, the architect should be put in the position he would have been in had the contract been fully performed. This would be a protection of his *expectancy* interest. Under this test, he would be entitled to his entire fee, based on full performance (determined by the contract rate times the estimated cost), less interim fee payments received and less the expense saved by him in not having to perform further. In addition, he would be entitled to any additional damages caused by the breach which was foreseeable at the time the contract was made.

An illustration would be commissions he might have been able to obtain had he completed the project. Perhaps he could show that other clients would have retained him, had he been able to show them the completed project, and that these clients were lost when the project was abandoned. Such evidence would *not* be relevant if, as in the AIA contract, the architect is given the privilege of abandoning the project.

Other possible recoverable items would be losses incurred due to the need for a sudden reduction in the architect's staff or the diminished productivity of personnel especially hired for the project who could not be immediately released. The architect would have to show causation and foreseeability to recover for these losses, however, and both are usually difficult to prove.

As an alternative to expectancy, the architect might be able to recover his *reliance,* or out-of-pocket expenses. This would normally be the reasonable value of the architectural services performed, without regard to future services. As a rule, like most professionals, this is all the architect will try to recover.

A provision of the current AIA contract permits the architect to recover the reasonable value for his services performed to date of discharge plus "terminal expenses" if the project is abandoned. This clause might be held to preclude his right to recover expectancy damages, if it was found that the contractual measure of recovery was exclusive. No cases have discussed this question. If the architect wishes to preserve his right to expectancy damages, this clause, if used, should be amended to state that it is not the exclusive remedy.

There may be a long-run advantage to using reliance as the exclusive remedy. Such a remedy emphasizes the professional nature of the architect-client relationship. Emphasis upon this might convince the court that a cost condition was not created, since the limited remedy and professional relationship are incompatible with the creation of a cost condition. This factor could be influential in close cases, leading a court to exclude evidence of a cost condition or to hold that no condition was imposed.

Interim fee payments raise the problem of divisibility. These payments, like progress payments to contractors, are not based upon precise value measurements, nor upon agreed valuations of the architect's services at the various stages of his performance. The payments are rough approximations, intended to give the architect operating funds during his often lengthy performance. When the architect sues to recover the reasonable value of his services prior to discharge, the interim fee payments received are deducted from the amount of his claim. If the reasonable value of the architect's services to the time of discharge is less than the amount of interim fee payments he has received, the client is entitled to a refund.

Actions against the Architect

Most of the reported appellate cases have involved actions by architects to recover their fees. In some instances, clients have asserted causes of action against the architect on incorrect cost estimates. Sometimes these actions are asserted independently against the architect, but more often they are the basis for counterclaim by the client when sued by the architect for fees. In such actions the material issues are:

1. Has the architect promised that the project could be built for a specified amount and that he will be accurate, or merely use due care?

2. What effect should be given to contract disclaimers?

3. Has the promise been performed?

4. What is the measure of the client's recovery?

In order not to lose a client, architects may, reluctantly and perhaps unwisely, risk their fee on the accuracy of their cost estimates. However, they usually do not intend to go farther by *promising* that the project can be built for a specified amount, nor that they will be accurate.

Normally, both architect and client assume that the architect will use due care in the performance of his work. Whether the architect has used due care depends upon the customary methods of measuring professional competence. He is held to the standard of care of others of his profession with his experience, judged by the standards of the community in which he practices.

Whatever effect disclaimers have upon the architect's right to collect his fee, disclaimers should certainly preclude any action against the architect for inaccuracy. However, disclaimer clauses should have no effect where the architect is negligent.

If the architect has breached, and the project is abandoned, the architect will not be able to collect for his services, since performance of his promise also conditions the client's promise to pay. Also, the client can recover any interim fee payments that have been made, as well as any reasonably foreseeable reliance expenses made valueless or less valuable due to abandonment of the project.

If the client proceeds with the project as designed, complications develop. Presumably, the client has not been damaged, since he has a project which is worth what it cost him. A court might use the diminished economic value of the project as a measure for the client's recovery, if this can be established.

If the project is completed by the client, a problem arises under the *rule of avoidable consequences*. Normally, damages which could have been reasonably avoided by the nonbreaching party (here the client) are not recoverable. Proceeding with the project should not constitute enhancing damages, unless the principal motive was to enlarge the architect's liability. Use of the plans by the client, by itself, should not constitute waiver of any cause of action the client may have for damages.

While use of the plans should not waive the client's right to recover for damages, use does affect the architect's right to be paid for his work. If the use of the plans is accompanied by evidence manifesting a waiver of the cost condition, the architect would be entitled to be paid under the contract. The measure of the architect's recovery in such a case would be the rate of commission times the cost of the project. If the use is not held to constitute waiver of the condition, the architect's measure of recovery would be based on quasi contract, or benefit conferred. The architect's breach is likely to cause the court to place a low value on the benefit conferred on the client by the use of the plans.

Any recovery for the use of the plans, whether based on contract or quasi contract, will be diminished or canceled out by any damages recoverable because of a breach by the architect. This discussion assumes a breach which has not been waived and for which damages are recoverable by the client.

Actions by the client for breach have been rare, and as a rule, unsuccessful. It should be recognized, however, that there is an unmistakable increase in the number of lawsuits against professional persons. Potentially, liability *does* exist for negligent cost estimates. This liability is often not covered by professional liability insurance, and cannot be insulated against by contract disclaimers.

Generally, the courts have not been sympathetic to architects. If architects want to avoid misunderstanding with clients over excessive costs and to heighten their chances of recovery if litigation should prove necessary, they should:

1. Make a conscientious and determined effort to come to a clear understanding with the client over their respective rights and duties with regard to costs of the project.

2. Express the understanding fully and clearly in the contract.

3. Keep the client informed about current cost estimates, with special reference to the effect changes are having on costs.

4. Keep detailed records of conversations and agreements with the client over costs.

PART THREE

*Systems and
Techniques for
Cost Control*

FIVE

George E. Kassabaum, FAIA

Methods for
Control of
Building Costs

No criticism of the architectural profession is heard more often than the charge that architects have too little regard for the client's dollar. It is said that too many members of the profession are generally incapable or careless in the matter of adhering to budgets, that they are not able to predict with reasonable accuracy the cost of a building which they design, and that they have a generally casual attitude about money. Because of this, many consider an architect to be someone whose services are sought when luxury can be afforded. However, if the project of the moment is to be one that must be built on a strict budget and handled in a businesslike way, then others who offer speed, certainty, and convenience may be the answer.

This is a criticism that literally hits us where we live, and the reasons for its popularity are many. The nature of reporting in the general press and in private conversation contributes to the persistence of the image. Occasions where building costs exceed the architect's estimate often make headlines—especially in public projects—and brisk conversation. On the other hand, the times when estimates are accurate and budgets are met are hidden on back pages or completely unreported or not discussed. It's the old story of bad news being big news, and good news being no news at all.

Advertising by those trying to undermine the profession also contributes to the bad impression. One prominent advertisement by one who offers a rival service uses the theme that if you come to him, you "know the cost before you start." The implication is that if you employ an architect, you won't know the cost until it's too late to do anything about it.

But a more compelling reason for the frequent repetition of this criticism is that it contains a core of truth. The profession as a whole is vulnerable on this point, and every conscientious architect must carefully evaluate his own performance in this area. There is a professional standard and responsibility to be met, and many of today's architects fall far short of it. We often fail to consider carefully enough the potential costs of a project, or we simply don't take seriously enough our responsibility to be expert in predicting and controlling construction costs.

Yet this is a problem that must deeply concern the profession as it faces increasingly severe competition from many directions. The critics and competitors rarely fail to spread the word when an architect does a bad job on any phase of cost control. Package builders, or contractors with architects on their staffs, who guarantee costs can hurt the profession badly in this area, and we simply must come to grips with the problem. If we fail to do so, we will suffer increased inroads from the competition. It may be fashionable to be vague about money, but it is neither practical nor responsible, nor does it contribute to the rosy future being predicted for architects.

Cost considerations are among the most basic considerations the architect must deal with. He is under a profound responsibility to see that the client's budget is adhered to and that the project is built within the cost forecast.

The most practical reason for this is that it is the only way that the architect can be sure that the building will be built. Cost has the final control over virtually every project. The client who gives the architect a free hand with money is rare, if he exists at all. Our firm has built a great many buildings, and we have never had an owner give us anything like a blank check. I suspect that the client who has endless faith in the architect and a bottomless purse is more a creature of historical imagination than of experience. Certainly today's corporate client is more sophisticated in matters of building costs than ever before. He is likely to have a staff architect, and he certainly will want to go over cost estimates with a fine-tooth slide rule. If the estimates don't measure up, the project will be in trouble before it starts.

In addition to these immediate and practical considerations of cost responsibility, there is a basic professional responsibility at issue. Accurate cost analysis and control is a very definite part of the professional service that the architect must render his client; failure to perform carefully in this area is no more excusable than providing inadequate mechanical facilities or not putting hardware on doors.

Each time the architect accepts a commission, he puts the reputation of the profession on the line along with his own. Any embarrassment he causes himself through careless or incapable cost control rubs off on *all* architects. Conversely, credit reflects on all.

Still another responsibility reflected in cost analysis and control is that which architects owe to the community. We *know* that our buildings will better serve both client and community than those "designed" by persons who sell expediency and neglect the human values. We *know* that if we surrender control of building to the competition, the community will suffer. Perhaps we even know that we deserve the professional damage, if we do not respond to the challenges—but certainly the community deserves better than those dreary packages.

Today's world is asking today's architects to be more than dreamers or men who know something about materials or who can find a solution to the building problem of the moment. Today's world is asking that the profession step to the front and provide the type of leadership that is necessary to lead tomorrow's masses out of today's messes. But leadership will not be bestowed upon the irresponsible, and one of the important responsibilities architects must accept is that of being the experts in the broad, general field of building construction.

Within this broad field, an age that has often been accused of worshiping tangible things is desperately looking for a group that can accurately predict the cost of any size and type of building project and keep the cost under control. By default, the architectural profession has allowed others, who—even at best—are no better qualified, to take the lead in the race to satisfy this need. Architects are often inclined to seek the cost information they need from a general contractor, an individual who may be knowledgeable in the cost of only the concrete and carpentry work and who depends on the advice of other specialists for the many other prices he needs. The so-called "general" contractor is more and more becoming a specialist, and as the construction field becomes more and more specialized, the need for a generalist is more and more apparent. This great opportunity should be seized by the architect.

Qualifications of the Estimator

The qualifications of the estimator can be, in theory, those of a Solomon. In practice, the basic requirements for the job are fairly straightforward.

The essential knowledge for an estimator is that of the construction process. The estimator should probably have worked on construction projects, so that he has some concept of, for example, the amount of labor involved in hanging a door or installing a window. This knowledge is important because labor prices are the most significant variables in the construction business and among the most difficult to forecast.

The estimator must be able to read drawings, both sketches and details, and as in the case of our chief estimator, his effectiveness will be greatly increased by having actually spent time on the drafting board. This gives a better insight into the complexities of the details and helps him to estimate better such things as the flashing and sash requirements, even though they may not be shown on the sketches in front of him.

In addition to information from the project architect, other help is available to the estimator. All the standard estimating references and textbooks are at his disposal. He finds them valuable as checkpoints, references, and guides, especially in the use of unfamiliar materials. But they should be used only as guides. Our experience has been that while these references are accurate within broad ranges, they are not geographically or chronologically specific enough for the precise sort of estimating that we seek.

The estimating job is most demanding and, on any scale, is not a job to be done only when time permits. Our own firm has established a department to perform this task. But any good architect in a small office who has a respect for his client's budget should be able to perform, in one way or another, the same task. It can be done through arrangement with a person hired on a consulting basis, or one of the staff architects can do this as one of his responsibilities.

Many architects are not disposed to do this sort of detail work and may prefer to employ someone to do the estimating. But whether it is done within or outside the architect's office, it is a responsibility of the architect, and as such, it is a task that must be done competently and accurately.

Assuming the desire and the ability, as in most things, there are good ways of going about performing the estimating service and ways that are not so good.

Factors in Good Estimating

Regardless of the method used, there are certain considerations that will have a material effect on the accuracy of the end product of estimating.

First, in a time when most architects have projects outside their own community, regional differences in availability, productivity of labor, and prices of materials can be a difficult factor to compute. If all architects were experts and were willing to share their information and experiences, the telephone would be all that was needed to feed the proper factors into the formulas. Until this is the case, there are publications, such as *Engineering News-Record*, that regularly publish labor rates, costs of materials, and indices. These, used with judgment, can be most helpful in overcoming the lack of familiarity with the practices in another place.

Second, there is the problem of evaluating the use of new techniques and materials. Too often, such new ideas are presented to persons in an architect's office who never get around to sharing their information with the man who eventually must predict the cost. This knowledge must be shared if the best results are to be obtained.

Another problem connected with new techniques and materials is that we have found that it is not safe to assume that the low bidder will evaluate the convenience or other potential savings of "the latest thing" in the same way that the enthusiastic salesman did. When a bidder puts his own money on the line, he tends to become highly conservative in his experiments with new practices, and since the bidder's figure is the one that will be used in determining whether the architect's estimate was accurate or not, we must be equally realistic in our analysis.

Newness is also connected with a third consideration, for the various trades respond to new techniques differently in different areas. Such jurisdictional rules may significantly alter the economy of certain practices. Setting of precast-concrete panels is a useful example. In one area, this work may be performed by one class of labor at a certain cost; in another area, control by a different union or disputes between the trades may result in more than one trade participating in the settling process, and any of these conditions may substantially alter the cost.

Differences in building codes may also have a great influence on construction costs. It is too much to expect that the estimator can be aware of all code provisions for all areas, but he should be aware of the possible influences that these regional differences may have on cost. Even if it is not possible to check on all these things at the time an estimate is needed, it is certainly important that the assumptions be reviewed carefully as the job moves through the office and more information is obtained.

Even such things as bidding practices can affect the final cost and should, therefore, be taken into consideration in the preparation of an estimate. There is much dispute over whether the lowest cost will be obtained by a single contract or whether separate bids are the best, and this is not the place to debate either side. However, depending upon the practices prevailing in the area and depending on the distribution of the work among the trades, as much as 3 percent of the cost of the building can be involved.

Each individual estimator would probably add a few other factors to this list, and this is what would make his technique different than that of another man in another office. It all adds up to the need for imagination and judgment in the preparation of an estimate and not to have the estimate be just a form to be filled in or a series of numbers to be added.

Now that we have the desire, the estimator, and an awareness of the variables, how does one make the estimate? As too many have found out, it is fatal to seek the "easy" way.

The Rules of Thumb for Estimating

Despite the practical and professional importance of cost estimating, many architects rely on cost estimating and control methods that are really inadequate. The most widely used and frequently mentioned of these are the so-called "rules of thumb." They include "unit cost," "volume cost," "cost per square foot," and others. Their advantage is that they are so easy and convenient. Their disadvantage is that no such easy method will do the proper job.

However, such methods are useful, for they can be of value early in a project before there is a program or drawings and when there is a minimum of information. Then, the rules of thumb, developed from similar experience, adjusted for time and place, and *used with caution,* may provide the only means of approximating the eventual project cost. But any architect who continues to put his faith in these methods throughout the preparation of the drawings is on shaky ground.

If they are used in this way, as a preliminary guide, both the architect and his client should clearly understand that the rules of thumb are only the most general of guidelines.

Cost per square foot, often used and widely quoted as an indication of building cost, is one of the most vague of these rules of thumb and one of the most risky to employ. It is not usually as indicative of building value as many believe it to be. And even if it were, individual architects have so many different ways of computing square footage that the cost figures can vary widely on a single project, depending on what system of determining square footage was used.

Even though the AIA has established a procedure for this computation, the number of methods actually used is probably nearly as great as the number of architectural practices. Of course this makes any cost-per-square-foot figure obtained from others essentially unreliable, and unfortunately, most clients' figures come from "others."

In our office, we have developed a square-foot method which we think is fairly sophisticated, and we adhere religiously to it. Although this method may partially reflect the sort of buildings that we design, it is reproduced here for whatever value it may be to others.

1. Areas must be figured on basis of both enclosed area and total area.

2. All areas must be figured from exterior face of wall to exterior face of wall.

3. Special areas as listed below must be figured on the basis of the following factors as applied to the actual area:

Attic areas, unfinished	0
Balconies	$\frac{1}{6}$
Basements, finished	Full
Basements, unfinished	$\frac{1}{2}$
Carports	$\frac{1}{3}$
Crawl spaces	$\frac{1}{8}$
Courts, enclosed on three or four sides	$\frac{1}{2}$
Garages, heated	$\frac{2}{3}$
Garages, unheated	$\frac{1}{2}$
Overhangs, building above	$\frac{1}{4}$
Overhangs, with sunscreen	$\frac{1}{4}$
Overhangs, roof	$\frac{1}{8}$
Penthouses	$\frac{1}{2}$
Porches, covered	$\frac{1}{3}$
Porches, enclosed	$\frac{2}{3}$
Terraces	0
Tunnels	$\frac{1}{8}$
Walkways, covered	$\frac{1}{3}$
Walkways, enclosed	$\frac{2}{3}$

Let me make it clear at this point that while we do not regard the cost-per-square-foot index as accurate enough for cost estimating, we do not reject it as a tool for discussion purposes. We have to be able to respond very quickly to cost inquiries that are made on a cost-per-square-foot basis. But we use it gingerly. As soon as possible we make it clear to the client that it is very difficult to be certain that we are comparing apples with apples and not with pears and that this method is only a rule of thumb which serves only as a general guide and a check on more precise methods of cost estimating.

If a client wants a building with, for example, 100,000 sq ft of rentable office space, we must be able to tell him very early approximately how much such a building will cost. Our past experience helps us to say that an office building will cost a minimum of $15 per sq ft, depending on quality and type of equipment; that a full-service hospital will cost $28 to $30 per sq ft with all the modern facilities installed; that a school can be built for $18 to $25 per sq ft, depending on the extent of the facilities required.

Other things must be understood as well. In the preparation of such preliminary cost approximations, it should be remembered that a client's program often is expressed in terms of net areas; both architect and client should be aware that the net rentable space in a structure is not the same as the total square-foot space that must be built. In early conversations, and on the basis of our methods of calculating square footage, we estimate that the total square footage in an office building will be about 50 percent more than the net rentable square footage.

The client should be weaned away from cost-per-square-foot estimates as soon as possible. The variables should be explained to him—the availability of utilities, the quality and amount of mechanical equipment, the quality of finishes, for example. But we are certainly prepared in initial discussions to give the owner a price range within which we can design a building.

For our own purposes, we use square-foot costs as a basis for determining whether the owner's preliminary budget is reasonable. And we always keep cost-per-square-foot figures as a check on our other estimates.

One sure way of helping the client to understand the hazards of reliance on cost per square foot is to explain how calculations on this basis can put a premium on inefficient design. If the building is poorly planned, with lots of wasted space, the costs of its more expensive areas—toilets, kitchens, bathrooms, other high-finish areas—are spread over a larger base, and the average cost per square foot will be lower. But the project cost, or other unit costs, may be high, and the job will be an expensive one, though the square-foot cost will be low. On the other hand, in an efficiently planned building with a minimum of waste space, the cost per square foot will be higher, though the total cost will be less.

Our policy is to make the owner a partner in the planning. When we can explain the problems of square-foot estimating to him, we can draw him away from total reliance on this method of cost estimating. But the concept of cost per square foot is too firmly established to be easily dismissed, and it has too much use for discussion purposes to be thrown out. There is, after all, no need to burden the client with all the intricacies of cost estimating. Complete education on this point would be both difficult and unnecessary. The point is that architects must be fully aware that this and other rules of thumb are inadequate for the task of accurate cost estimating.

Many of the same hazards occur if volume computations are used as a rule of thumb. Volume computations may be more difficult to make and may sound more impressive, but most of the problems and shortcomings inherent in the cost-per-square-foot computation are also present in the volume-cost system. In our office, we do compute volume costs and record them. However, we do this for additional guidance in the early planning stages of a program. These are the factors that we use:

1. Areas are computed on the same basis as is used in calculating square footage.

2. Vertical measurements are from the bottom of the floor slab, if the slab is on grade, or from the surface of the crawl space to the top of the roof deck on buildings with flat roofs and to the point two-thirds between lowest and highest points on buildings with pitched roofs.

3. Other volumes are computed on the basis of the following figures as applied to the actual volume:

Areaways	$\frac{1}{2}$
Balconies	0

Another rule-of-thumb method widely used is the "unit-of-use" method—the cost per bed, per student, per desk, or some other relationship which expresses the cost not in terms of area but in terms of use. This method has obvious advantages. However, if a building is inefficiently designed to house 100 students, the cost per square foot could be very low, while the cost per unit of use could be extremely high. But the result of such a computation is again, at best, only a vague guideline for predicting particular project costs; too many individual factors influence each project to make this a reliable tool.

In fact, there are hazards involved in using any of these rules of thumb in client conferences. Your client will always have heard, through one or another of those channels of inaccurate information, about a building very nearly like the one he wants that was built at a cost of so much per square foot—almost certainly a low cost per square foot—and he wants you to assure him that you can match that figure. On the other hand, the various rules of thumb can serve as useful guidelines to both architect and client in the early stages of planning and be of continuing use as reference points as the project moves along. But they lack the precision required for really accurate estimates that an architect can stand behind morally, professionally, personally, and, if necessary, legally.

The architect's personal judgment is simply not adequate to the job of cost estimating. More scientific methods must be used. Fortunately, these are available. But, as might be expected, they are not easy.

Quantity Survey

The experience in our office has convinced us that the only estimating method that is accurate and reliable enough for good architectural practice is the quantity-survey method. We are convinced that the architect must employ the services of a skillful estimator and have him take off from drawings the quantities of the various materials needed for the project. The estimator must determine what the cost of those materials will be when they are put in place. As the end result of this fairly long and detailed process, the estimator will produce an accurate determination of what the cost of the building will be.

Although our practice is fairly large, with a two-man estimating department, quantity-survey cost estimating need not, nor should it, be confined to large architectural practices. Every office that hopes to fulfill its professional and client responsibilities must do much the same thing in estimating that we do in our office.

The quantity-survey–estimate work begins with the designer. In the ance of realistic and practical control over project cost. Only an approach that accepts responsibility for a good deal of detail work will accomplish the job. Yet, even with careful attention to all this detail, cost estimating remains essentially a creative task.

The quantity-survey—estimate work begins with the designer. In the early studies of the program, and in preparation of early concepts, time does not ordinarily permit the designer to check, in detail, the probable costs of every concept. But he should have a good idea of the probable costs if he uses, for example, steel framing structure, reinforced concrete, brick bearing walls, or wood frame. The more mature the designer, the better his judgment will be. Ideally, he develops what might almost be called a sixth sense for cost. These unmeasured judgments represent all the cost control feasible until some drawings have been produced. Then these preliminary designs may be checked with the estimator.

The designer draws up the building, showing the functional layout, usually in single-line diagrams, showing partitions, windows, sizes of rooms. An elevation drawing is made that shows heights of stories, configuration of windows, and exterior materials. The greater the number of dimensions that can be indicated on these drawings, the more accurately the estimator can work. The basic requirement of these drawings is that they define the building in terms of area and volume, basic structural system, and finishes. The drawings need not be in finished form at this stage. Simple prints should suffice. Sometimes, actual presentation drawings are used. In that case, they are more refined, but this is not essential. The basic requirement is that the scope of the work be clearly defined. This can be accomplished on a rough paper sketch as well as on precisely prepared presentation drawings.

Complete information required for the most accurate estimate possible will not be available until the final drawings are completed. This is where the creative quality of the estimator's work first becomes apparent. He must be able to convert these rather simple drawings into information that will enable him to forecast, accurately, what the construction costs will be after the design has been developed in much greater detail.

Good communication between the project architect or designer and the estimator is extremely important at this time. The estimator must clearly understand what the building is going to be. All his questions must be answered.

Naturally, the larger the project, the more acute the problems. A minor misjudgment on the cost of a window, for example, will be multiplied on a large building and minimized on a small one.

Many intangibles come into play at this point. The estimator must be aware of cost trends, for instance. He must be familiar with the tradition within the office, knowing that certain kinds and quality of hardware are likely to be used on certain buildings. Anything unique or even unusual must be thoroughly discussed.

Soon after the owner approves the preliminary package, the project architect, the designer, the mechanical engineers, and the specifications writers meet to discuss the building in great detail. This meeting is intended to ensure that everyone knows what the building is to be like and what the estimate should include.

On the basis of this understanding and these drawings, the estimator goes to work. He begins to build the building, in a sense, working on the basis of his calculations.

If possible, the estimator should visit the site as an early step in his work. Unusual site characteristics may have a significant influence on his estimate. A heavily wooded site that must be cleared or a place that is difficult to reach or has complicated terrain will have great influence on the estimate. It has been our experience that the most common source of estimating error is found on the site itself.

If the estimator cannot actually go to the site, topographic surveys and aerial photographs should be provided for him.

Because the cost of the structure may be as much as one-third the cost of the finished building, calculating its cost is the way most of our estimates begin. On simple structures, the spacing and sizing may be determined by the use of handbooks. Structures of most conventional buildings can be computed in terms of weights and volumes of materials needed to support the live and dead loads. On the basis of these calculations and upon general assumptions about the probable bearing capacity of the soils, the estimator can arrive at a reasonably accurate prediction about the cost of foundation and structure.

Often this work is done in cooperation with manufacturers and fabricators, but figures obtained in this way must be checked with care, for the architect is professionally responsible for the figures he uses, regardless of their source.

Later, a structural engineer, armed with findings of test borings and more detailed studies of loads, will determine structural requirements in greater detail and with more precision. The estimator should be able, at this stage, to arrive at a figure within 3 to 5 percent of the final cost of the structure. Since the structure represents roughly one-third of the building costs, this is an important accomplishment.

With foundation, site, and structure costs compiled, the estimator theoretically encloses the building. Costs of exterior walls, including sash and glazing, exterior materials, etc., are determined. Roofing and insulation costs are estimated. Quantities of wall materials, flooring, and similar material requirements are computed.

This process can be about as detailed and complex as one cares to make it. To illustrate, let me present some of the items on the checklist used in our estimating department.

We attempt to estimate such job expenses as protection of the project while it is being constructed, cost of temporary facilities including heat, electricity, and other utilities. The price of the earth moving which will be required is calculated. Demolition costs are estimated. These costs can vary greatly, because of insurance expenses and the ease or difficulty of removing from the site and disposing of any previous buildings or materials.

As an example of the length this checklist can assume, here are our checkpoints under the heading of miscellaneous iron: steel stairways including rails, handrailings, stair railings, fire escapes, window guards, corner guards, lintels, thresholds, miscellaneous iron in connection with carpentry, iron in connection with heating system, steel roof deck, and other.

Masonry, carpentry and millwork, roofing and sheet metal, plaster work, metal work, ornamental metal, waterproofing and dampproofing, glass and glazing, acoustic work, floor coverings, tile, marble and terrazzo, painting, elevators or moving stairs, subdrainage system, radiation protection—all these have similar lists of items that must be estimated.

Outside the building but still part of the project are such potential expenses as site preparation and improvements, roads and parking area, sidewalks, railroad trackage, sewers, water distribution lines, hot water or steam lines, electrical installations, and fire-alarm system.

When the costs of all these materials have been estimated, the estimator has theoretically built the building just as logically and completely as would a contractor.

Mechanical and Electrical Estimates

Mechanical and electrical work will also represent about one-third, or more, of the building cost. Rules of thumb in this area—rules like cost per electrical outlet, cost per plumbing fixture, cost per ton of air conditioning—are no better in providing an accurate estimate for this portion of the work than they are in arriving at the total cost.

Again, the quantity-survey method must be used to determine carefully the amount of electrical wiring and plumbing, the number of outlets, amount of duct required for air-conditioning system and heating plant, lighting fixtures, etc.

The mechanical and electrical engineers with whom we work insist that it is simply impossible to make a precise estimate of the costs of the materials on the basis of the preliminary drawings. These drawings are at best diagrammatic, they say, and it is not possible for the engineers, relying solely on them, to measure the feet of cable and wiring and conduit. Thus, for their first estimate, they rely on a less sophisticated way of measuring—using average number of wires per outlet and tonnage of air conditioning, for example, and employ these data to come up with an estimate.

The procedure at this stage is of the same nature as that of the designer who, in the early stages of the project, relies on experience and broad rules as a guide to building costs. Both the designer and the mechanical engineer make more exact estimates as soon as possible.

Their basic problem, the engineers say, is that until mechanical drawings are complete, it is impossible to determine the precise amount of material that will be needed to equip the building. They rely, as a result, on rules of thumb that are even more flexible than general construction estimates. Of course when the drawings are complete, they are able to make their estimates with accuracy comparable to those made for other parts of the building.

The tradition of architectural design within a firm can cause costs to vary by 10 percent, say the engineers. If the architect (or the owner) is willing to leave pipes or wiring exposed, for example, the cost will probably be less than if all utilities are concealed. If an architect is particularly adept at providing ample spaces for ducts and piping and conduit, the engineer can install the equipment at a lower cost than if these spaces are tight or difficult to adapt mechanical equipment to.

Even though estimating this phase of the work is, in the early stages of the project, less precise than desirable, one thing that keeps architects out of more serious trouble at the end is the tremendous range of selectivity available in cost of equipment. Pumping equipment, for example, can vary in cost by 100 percent. The cheaper equipment will probably wear out quicker and be more expensive to maintain, but it will do the job in the case where holding down the first costs is the most important consideration. Refrigeration equipment, for another example, can be provided for anywhere from $90 to $200 a ton, depending on type, quality, durability, and operating expense. The most expensive is often cheaper in the long run, but the fact that the lower-cost equipment is available provides a factor that can help the mechanical engineer work within a budget.

It is, of course, the responsibility of either the mechanical engineer or the architect to explain to the client this variation in equipment cost. It would be improper to install lower-cost equipment, with its attendant high operating and replacement cost, without informing the client.

Many other variables exist in mechanical equipment. Complicated controls may add to the comfort of heating and cooling in a building, but they raise construction costs. The number of zones into which a building is divided for air-treatment purposes falls in the same category.

Quality of ductwork, wiring, and plumbing can also be varied, but the total saving available in this area is much less than that which can be obtained by varying the basic quality of equipment.

Utility costs are often difficult, or even impossible, for the engineer to determine in preliminary stages of planning. A large laboratory installation, for example, requires extensive electric, gas, and disposal facilities. If an adequate electric substation is convenient, if a large gas pipeline is nearby, and if an adequate sewage system is available, costs will be far lower than if these utilities must be provided by the owner. The resulting variable in a building cost estimate can amount to $100,000 or more on a major project. For various reasons, early estimates may be required without going to the time and expense of making a full investigation of the availability of such services. And the engineer is likely to find himself in a position where he will have to simply make a guess. If he is skillful, that guess can be reasonably accurate. But this portion of the estimate should be reviewed with caution and special care when detailed information becomes available.

Since the engineers may not have had much contact with the owner at the time of the first estimate and since the accuracy of this part of the estimate will be directly related to the amount of information available, the architect should find certain answers, including the following:

1. *Volume and Area of the Building* This is the basic factor which will enable him to determine the number of BTUs of heating and cooling that will be required.

2. *Type of Occupancy* A building with a large number of active occupants will have different heating and cooling requirements than a less heavily occupied building.

3. *Type of Equipment* Some machines produce considerable excess heat; this must be compensated for both in winter and in summer.

Ideally, the owner will provide a list of equipment with its heat-generating factor and the power required, although such detail is not likely to be available in the early stages of planning.

4. *Glass and Insulation* Structures with double-pane, heat-resisting glass and heavy insulation elsewhere have far different requirements than those with less costly windows and walls.

5. *Lighting* The choice of incandescent or fluorescent lighting can have a startling effect on heat requirements; the recent interest in heating office buildings through light fixtures is an example of the possible variations in this area.

6. *Air Change* High-velocity systems that change air often, either for comfort or to expel air from laboratories, are more expensive than systems with lower air-change requirements.

7. *Power Requirements* Simple offices and classroom buildings have much lower power requirements than laboratory, or even residential, structures. The difference is reflected in utility costs.

When all of these factors, and many lesser ones, have been taken into consideration, it becomes apparent that the task of the mechanical engineer is difficult when he has all the information; it is virtually impossible for him to make an accurate guess on the basis of limited information.

Perhaps we should be glad that an experienced engineer can make estimates as accurately as he does. But the real professional responsibility is to devise a system that will provide the engineer with the sort of information he needs for more accuracy, as soon as possible and in the greatest amount possible.

This process—never a simple one—has become increasingly more complicated in recent years, as the proportion of the building dollar spent on mechanical and electrical components has increased. There was a time when a building required a heating plant, wiring for electric lights, and telephone wiring. Now, the building is generally air-conditioned as well as heated, the electrical requirements extend not just to lighting but to power for additional office or commercial equipment, and the telephone system must often be supplemented with additional communications systems. In some cases, these additional utility costs are extremely difficult to assess.

It is essential in this area of building design that estimating become more sophisticated. More and more of the building dollar goes for these components—we once calculated that 30 percent of the building dollar was spent in that area, and now it is often 50 percent. Thus, if these calculations are inaccurate as a result of reliance on general area cost per square foot or some other rule of thumb, the architect's overall estimate is certain to be in error.

Growth and Improvement Factor

All buildings tend to grow in complexity and size as design moves from preliminaries to working drawings. Compliance with codes may widen a stair, add a toilet, or require additional fireproofing. Probably the biggest factor is the architect's own desire to have everything exactly right. Because of this tendency, every preliminary estimate should include a "growth and improvement" factor of about 3 percent. Unless the project architect is unusually alert, failing to provide this factor may result in the sort of inaccurate estimate that has so often been attributed to architects by the public.

On the other hand, obviously an architect cannot overestimate. A client has just as much right to feel cheated if his bids come in too low. He feels that he could have had more building for his budget, and he may well ask why he didn't get it. This is especially true in the case where bond issue money or governmental appropriations are involved, for public bodies are obligated by law to make the best use of money entrusted to their keeping.

Finally, all the pieces are ready to be put together in a complete estimate. The estimator must then evaluate the conditions that will most likely prevail at the time bids are received and add sums to cover the contractor's overhead and profit. I feel that this is largely where the low bidder and high bidder separate; since the percentage for these items used in the bid will vary, depending upon the work load in each bidder's office, his own desires, and many other personal considerations that are impossible to predict, an estimator in an architect's office should use an average figure.

Even then, the figures used will vary, depending upon the size of the job. In our office, we adjust for this, but the base from which we deviate is 8 percent for overhead and 5 percent for profit. A hungry bidder will settle for less, but sound judgment in applying these factors should produce the desired result—neither the lowest nor the highest figure, but one within the bidding range.

After the Estimate

After the project has been given approval by the owner, the estimate must be constantly reviewed to ensure that it remains valid. Again, the project architect, designer, mechanical engineer, electrical engineer, structural engineer, and the specification writers should meet to go over the assumptions, determine the level of quality, and review decisions so that each part of the team clearly understands the budget limitations he is expected to meet. This is another time when questions must be asked and answers determined.

Such responsibility cannot be shared; therefore, in our office, it is the responsibility of the project architect to be as certain as possible that the project is presented for bid in a form that will meet the budget. It is his judgment that determines whether any changes carried out are basic enough to require additional estimates. It is surprising to me to see how many changes are regularly made in a plan after the preliminary design is approved. Basements can be added, expanded, or taken away; crawl spaces can be added or supplemented, and other changes that could substantially alter the project cost are made.

It is clearly the responsibility of the project architect to confer with the client regarding any important change made in the project during the period between approval and bidding. The client may order changes that could add to the expense. If so, the project architect must prepare him for a possible cost increase.

As previously mentioned, we have learned that buildings tend to grow in size and improve in quality as the detailed drawings and specifications are developed. The client or the project architect tends to make small changes as the project moves along. These changes always seem to add to the total cost—a few more electric outlets or wires, a better-labeled door, another utility closet, or even an additional couple of feet in size.

Since a bad estimate is as serious a defect as a leaky roof, the project architect must be alert to the effect of today's decisions on yesterday's estimate. Even during the bidding, items on an addendum can affect the price; thus no one can relax until the bids are in. Even then, the relaxation will be short-lived, for costs must be kept under control until the construction of the building has been completed. At that juncture, if all those involved have done their jobs, everyone will be happy, and the profession's prestige will have been increased. A contribution will have been made, too, to an area of the architectural profession that is of special importance—the strengthening of its reputation for overall competence. I cannot state too strongly how important I think it is to improve our competence in the areas in which we already practice, and to expand our abilities to meet changing conditions. It is not fashionable to be vague, because it is not economic. Every time we yield an area of competence to another part of the building industry, we cut a piece from the foundation of our profession.

SIX

John R. Diehl, AIA

The Enclosure Method
of Cost Control

After all has been read, digested, and done by an architect about his problems of construction cost prediction, nothing can detract from the sometimes unbeautiful nakedness of the truth expressed in his bid tabulations. Finding out that a program is too large or too small for its budget at the bid stage is much too late.

Architects as well as builders, bankers, brokers, and owners have long sought effective means for predetermining the cost and economic value of buildings. The subject of almost universal speculation has been early prediction of costs for projected construction, or how to judge the potential cost of ideas. A number of people in history have undoubtedly justified their whole lives by simply worrying in advance about the possible costs of such things as the pyramids of Giza, the Acropolis, and the plans for Pompeii. Untold amounts of time and effort, some not so serious, have been devoted to the search for some simple secret that would provide insight into the vital mysteries of what is often a popular guessing game. Every operative involved with a proposed structure risks possibly more on the accuracy of preconstruction cost estimates than on any other group of unknown factors encountered in building. The methods of cost prediction they use currently range from the most involved and intricate systems of mathematical projection to ludicrous schemes based upon superstition, and sometimes even cynicism.

Some knowledgeable people hold that the accuracy of early construction cost prediction methods bears little relation to the complexity or degree of detail involved in the preparation of an "estimate." Who will deny the foolishness of analyzing the cost of *flemish bond* at a time when it is not known whether the wall in question will contain *bricks*? This writer remains impressed by the often quoted advice given, half in jest, to him and others years ago, by the late Harvey Wiley Corbett, the noted architect, to the effect that by far the most convenient index of building-construction cost is the current cost of beefsteak. Mr. Corbett pretended to insist that to determine the probable cost of any project as accurately as by any other method, one had only to multiply the volume of the structure in cubic feet by a price supplied by the local butcher. Few architects will risk the consequences of budget overrun with cost-control practices as elementary as this, but many are also painfully aware that the most elaborate and sophisticated estimating procedures are likely to be even less helpful in the early stages of the design process.

It is indeed one thing to anticipate a wide difference in the prices bid by various contractors for the construction of a proposed building that has been so completely described in its documents that it allows estimators to count virtually every nail, and quite another thing to expect a designer to predict costs with greater accuracy at a time when a blank sheet of drawing paper lies before him. Yet, it is at this point in the development of a project that the architect makes decisions most vitally affecting his client's budget.

In fact, more often than not, construction cost limitations are set even before the design problems that must be solved are fully known. Regardless of this technical dilemma, construction costs are necessarily controlled in the predesign stages, a fact which accommodates the basis upon which most building enterprises are undertaken. So, whether it can be easily accepted or not, it is clear that architects are the ones elected to bear certain added economic responsibilities which compound the cost-prediction problems already inherent in building design.

Problems of cost projection vary with different purposes; known procedures match the different problems only approximately and in varying degrees. The real estate appraiser employs quite different methods than does either the contract estimator or the financial planner. Building design is a special case, the conditions of which fit none of the more widely used cost-estimating systems. The importance of cost prediction to rational decisions in the selection of the materials and methods of construction is understood to be fundamental to architecture. However, cost prediction is not easily accomplished during the design, for none of the more analytical methods of cost projection can be employed by the architect until his work is finished. It is clearly uneconomical to produce the several complete designs that would be necessary for comparative evaluation by the quantity-takeoff and pricing methods used by contractors for bidding. To determine the probable cost of a building that has already been designed and adequately documented, an estimator will, most likely, separate the project into construction operations and price material separately from labor in the units by which they are normally purchased. Cubic feet of sand and gravel would be priced on a different market than carpentry labor, and so on. Sensitive and accurate though this method may be for the builder, it is relatively useless to the designer who must predict outcome before there are such quantities to consider.

The design process itself seems to allow the possibility of a "solution" on the first trial; the economic structure of the profession assumes this; at any rate, most architects approach each design study as potentially the final one. Actually to accomplish this obviously requires an act of synthesis by the designer which takes construction costs into account along with the other design considerations. Since even the most creative persons are obligated to control inductive thought by standards which are derived analytically, designers in all fields have developed various abstract devices to guide their thoughts, including those concerning costs, along rational and realistic routes through the maze of alternatives presented by their imaginations. A statistical approach is automatically taken on quantitative matters to afford prediction of effect without requiring immediate empirical data as the basis for each decision. Cost, like the other quantitative elements of a design problem, is reduced, often intuitively, to units that can be expressed in terms of function and performance in order to economize on the mental process. Thus, designers are prone to talk of: "tons" of refrigeration, "footcandles" of light, "square feet" of floor area, "pounds of load" supported per unit of material, "cubic feet" of air moved per minute, and the like—and of cost in terms of such units.

The architectural designer wants to know the cost of a material in its functional place, not merely its price on the market. The cost information most helpful to him is the total cost of an element of structure as it will exist in his building, including labor, material, and builders' charges. He would like this information in terms of such units as square feet of surface and lineal feet of span or length, the units by which he measures his own work. The architect can make choices between floor finishes by comparing the total in-place cost of one material with another, and will select a method of floor construction by comparing the combined in-place cost per unit of floor surface of all components of one floor system with the cost of others. In order to make this type of comparison, the architect collects cost information from a variety of sources and converts it to statistics in his own form. In this way each designer tends to develop a personal cost vocabulary.

Even formal construction cost estimates of completed design work prepared by architects nowadays are usually derived by this procedure, which is often referred to as the "In-Place Cost Method of Estimating." Although the actual cost information upon which this procedure is ultimately based must come from standard quantity-surveying and pricing methods, seldom does the architect himself analyze costs in terms of market units. He never estimates the cost of materials separately from the cost of labor, since he neither buys and sells building materials nor hires and supervises construction labor. He tries to maintain a comprehensive notion of the total value or cost of construction, rather than of the specific productivity or cost of skilled labor, or the cost and yield per board foot of a particular grade of lumber, and the like. He likes the vantage point which provides an objective view of the product together with its parts. He has seen the products of his own design completed; he knows how they have performed; he has found out what they have cost and has analyzed the effects of their alternatives. Designers are aware that approaching cost in terms of the units of function or effectiveness, e.g., how much wall to do what for how much money, relates performance to price directly and simplifies the evaluation of alternatives.

While predicting costs by the in-place method is certainly more convenient for the designer than some systems, it noticeably is more reliable when supported by detailed analysis. The cost of a wall is the sum of the costs of its components; the determination of these, again, is possible only in the more advanced stages of design. It must be clear that the more detailed the analysis of a green design, the more design information must have been available. The in-place method is therefore found to be of greatest value in the intermediate stages of design, after conceptual work and before detailed design has been completed.

This, of course, still leaves the architect without the tool he needs most: a reliable and convenient procedure for quick cost comparison on which to base early decisions, in order to reduce costly trial and error. This need leads to the universal use of even more abstract cost units. The most elementary such unit, and perhaps the most widely used throughout the building industry for rule-of-thumb estimating, appraising, and programming purposes, is *cost per square foot of floor area*. The reasons for the popularity of this unit are obvious: first, cost is thus expressed in terms of floor space, which is recognized as the primary functional quantity of most buildings; and second, floor area is easily and quickly measured either on drawings, in existing buildings, or even projected in the imagination as an abstract quantity. Thus, the proposer of a projected building may well have a notion of the amount of floor space required long before any thought has been given to the configuration of the structure. By guessing at a price per square foot, construction budgets are often established even before the architect is consulted. The architect himself generally makes extensive use of this convenient unit-of-building-cost measure for one purpose or another throughout his design work, most particularly during the schematic stage.

Be this as it may, it does not follow that because the quantity of space (floor area) in a building is some measure of its utility, the cost of the building will be directly, or even closely, related to this quantity. The fact that *it is not* will be recognized immediately upon observing that this unit cost varies widely from building to building, ranging in 1966 from less than $8 per sq ft of floor area for simple structures to more than $40 for highly subdivided and expensively equipped build-ings. In addition, wide discrepancies are easily introduced because of variations in accepted, standard definitions of measurable floor area. De-pending on many factors of design, function, and the method of measure, one idea of the floor area of a given building may exceed another by 100 percent or more. Most experts will agree that predicting construction costs by estimating the probable price per square foot of floor area is, at best, a sketchy procedure and, if not accompanied by the most cautious and experienced judgment, can be dangerous. In any event, the unit has not fulfilled the architect's need for cost information and control.

Another statistical method of this form which has long been applied to early cost prediction involves the measurement of the geometric vol-ume of buildings. While perhaps both less sensitive and more complex in procedure than the floor-area method, this system also chooses its units in terms of building space. But since space measured by volume is, for obvious reasons, less directly related to utility or function than is floor area and since the same additional disadvantages pertain, the method is now considered by many to be inferior.

Although not currently so widely used as the preceding examples of statistical estimating, the use of units of *enclosure* has been gaining acceptance in recent years as a method more satisfactory to the designer. This newer approach to early cost prediction requires slightly more complex procedures than the floor-area-unit method but no more so than in the measurement of cubic contents. The enclosure-unit method is both more sensitive and more accurate than either of the other two statistical methods. It has the additional advantage of being applicable at almost any stage of design and is adaptable to cost analysis in varying degrees of detail.

The procedure is to collect cost data in terms of units of enclosure surface, i.e., square feet or square yards of exterior walls, partitions, floors, roof, etc. These units vary determinately with respect to the functional units of building space on one hand, and to the quantities of construction materials on the other. For practical purposes it may be assumed that the bulk of materials and labor employed in a building is actually represented by its enclosure. If this is true, we have a unit of measure that is highly sensitive to variations in not only the amounts and, therefore, the costs of labor and materials represented by a given design, but also the amount of building space provided. The convenience of this method for the prediction of costs is easily demonstrated. Given sufficient statistical information and a knowledge of construction-cost factors, a designer can correlate cost with performance information for the solution of a specific problem very quickly. For example, an architect working on the design of a floor plan with enclosure costs in mind knows constantly how much money he is spending, virtually, as he draws lines indicating walls and partitions.

As when using floor-area units, however, those who use this method must understand that a line representing 3 lineal ft of partition, 9 ft high, not only involves certain quantities of several materials and types of labor but also represents prices, which vary independently of the quantities. The extent of this variation must be known or assumed if specific construction systems are to be compared. Herein lies the need for the designer's understanding of the various factors affecting the cost of construction. Herein also lies another advantage of the system: it can be expanded in later stages of design to become in-place cost estimating. For overall cost control, however, necessary corrections of this type tend to be smaller than the normal variations of other units and much more readily accommodated.

The writer, in his own architectural practice, has made use of this method of cost prediction in all stages of the design of a substantial number of projects over the past twelve years. These have ranged from simple residential alterations to multibuilding complexes costing more than 20 million dollars and from simple, open structures to highly subdivided and complex structures, such as hospitals. In addition to these, the drawings for numerous other projects as well as literally hundreds of scheme variations have been analyzed by the enclosure method. Adjusted to 1965 dollars, the actual costs of completed projects in this experience have ranged from a low of $3.60 to a high of $9.30 per sq ft of total enclosure area. This figure is derived by dividing the sum of all related construction expenditures by the total combined area of all floors, roofs, walls, partitions, and similar items of enclosure. It will be noted that these unit costs vary upward from the low figure to approximately 2.6 times the low figure, that variation should be compared with a conservatively estimated normal variation in floor-area-unit costs of more than 5 times. In other words, buildings vary in cost per square foot of floor area in the order of from $8 to $10, while enclosure-unit costs vary only half as much. Since no attempt was made to correct for inordinately disparate examples included among the projects recorded, normal experience will likely show an even smaller variation in costs per unit of enclosure among building types.

The mensuration involved is simple enough. The area of planes passing through and parallel to each element of enclosure is measured in square feet. An enclosure element is taken to be the sum of its components and may be any exterior wall, partition or interior wall, roof, or the like. The enclosure area represented by a floor system, for example, is expressed as the area of a single plane, whether or not the system includes separate ceiling and deck elements. Similarly, walls and partitions are measured as having a single surface; both faces are included in the one measurement. Consistent rules must be applied in dealing with stairs and other special items.

The data-collection procedure is also simple. Horizontal elements, such as floors and roofs, are measured from drawings in the same way floor area is normally determined. While the area of vertical elements, such as walls and partitions, can sometimes be taken from elevation or section drawings in a similar fashion, experience has revealed it to be more convenient to use plan drawings for all measurements. The total combined length of partitions is taken from the plan and multiplied by the partition height. The length of exterior walls is multiplied by the story height. The use of a dial-type "linometer" or "plan-measure" is most efficient for this purpose, being sufficiently accurate and much faster than either scaling or the tabulating of dimensions. With standard procedures and a minimum of practice, the amount of building enclosure represented by any plan drawn to scale, regardless of its sketchiness or refinement, can be determined almost in a matter of minutes.

Each scheme study, as well as later plan studies of all design projects, should be measured for comparison. A standard form should be used for recording the information. In general it will be found useful to record the data by floors, using a summary form to consolidate the figures for the entire structure. Partition, wall, floor, and roof totals should be tabulated separately so that maximum use can be made of the data for additional estimating and analytic purposes. The *enclosure quantity,* and combination of this with other building quantities, provides a number of interesting opportunities for advantageous design study that the architects who use them will come to appreciate.

For enclosure to serve the purpose of cost projection effectively, the user must understand certain things about the nature of the quantity itself. He must also agree to certain rules. For example, if it is to be granted that building costs do, in fact, vary somewhat directly with the amount of enclosure area, the following must also be accepted:

1. Building cost C is the total of all costs of construction chargeable to the *space-enclosing structure* itself, including fixed mechanical and electrical equipment but specifically excluding such items as land costs, site-improvement costs, owner's administrative expenses, furniture, and other costs not clearly related to enclosure.

2. Enclosure E is the total quantity of all defining elements of the structure as described above, measured in square feet. Items of enclosure include walls, partitions, floors, and roof. Columns, piers, stairs, railings, stacks, and similar integral items of construction should also be included, provided that consistent methods of measurement and calculation of equivalent quantities are used.

3. The enclosure unit cost c is the quotient resulting from the division structure as described above, measured in square feet. Items of enclosure E or: $c = C/E$.

4. All units of enclosure are assumed to have the same value, which is to say, a square foot of partition is taken to represent the same cost as a square foot of roof, exterior wall, parapet, or balcony.

It may be noted that partitions, for example, ordinarily cost less per unit to construct than exterior walls. In the overall sense, this difference is largely compensated for by the fact that building cost C represents all construction components, including mechanical and electrical work. In this connection, it will be observed that a building subdivided into small spaces by partitions, even though the partitions be of relatively inexpensive construction, requires more electrical outlets and switches, more doors and hardware, more heating and ventilating controls and outlets, and the like, than does an unsubdivided space. These extra costs are assumed to be chargeable to partition work, thus tending to equalize the unit construction cost.

The fact that variations in unit enclosure costs are smaller than the variations in other unit costs of this general type attests, somewhat, to the validity of this assumption.

The enclosure unit cost of a warehouse will be closer to a similar unit cost for an apartment building than the respective costs per square foot of floor area of the two building types as noted before. The reason probably is that the primary difference in the latter is affected more by amount of wall area per unit of floor area than by the actual construction cost of walls. Although it may seem contradictory, it is on this basis that it is further assumed that such variations as do exist in the enclosure unit costs of different buildings tend to represent closely actual differences in the quality of construction. One could therefore expect to be far more correct in estimating the probable cost of a hospital by the application of enclosure cost units derived from the analysis of a warehouse than by trying to adjust the floor-area unit costs of the warehouse for the same purpose. Under less exaggerated extremes of comparison, the architect can look forward to a broad range of inter-changeability in unit enclosure costs among different building types and therefore measurably extend the effects of his cost experience.

On the matter of measuring architectural elements having either non-planar or complex forms, the individual must use his best judgment in arriving at reasonably equivalent quantities. Because the units and quantities of enclosure will be found to have other useful applications in design study if kept reasonably close to geometric truth, factoring as a means of determining equivalent quantities should be avoided. In estimating the cost of a building by the floor-area method, the space in basements, or other unfinished sections, is often equated to more expensive space by arbitrarily reducing the measured quantity. There is no need to resort to such devices when dealing with enclosure. A stair, for instance, can be reduced to a quantity of enclosure simply by measuring the total area of all treads, risers, landings, and railings. Treads and landings of course are equal to the floor area occupied by the stairwell on each floor; riser area equals one-half the vertical cross section of the stairwell; railing area in a typical, equal-run stair tower approximately equals the area of a vertical plane taken longitudi-nally between the landings. Free-standing piers or columns are usually measured by vertical planes running with the greatest width. Built-in cabinets or case-work are sometimes measured as a second wall. No inter-ruption is recognized for windows, doorways, or similar wall openings.

Furred spaces, toilet partitions, and the like are debatable, but, how-ever these may be regarded, the estimator of enclosure quantities must, as noted before, follow consistent rules for his determinations if the information derived is to have widest application in his work. As use of the method becomes more widespread, combined experience no doubt will tend to establish universal rules and standards of procedure which will, hopefully, enhance the interchangeability of data throughout the profession.

In addition to being a quick and effective way to measure the quantity of construction and the probable cost represented by a design, the quan-tity of enclosure can also be easily related to floor area, the other quan-tity so highly representative of primary building function. This provides the architect with an even broader analytic tool, one that will dig even deeper at the beginning of design. Moreover, it is accomplished with little or no additional work, since, if a proper tabulation is made of the enclosure as taken from the drawings, floor area can always be identified as a separate item. For this purpose, relationship between the two quantities is established by the ratio e of floor area A to total enclosure E

$e = E/A$ = the number of enclosure units yielding one unit of floor space.

Much can be learned about the general geometric characteristics as well as the economics of a building simply by knowing this ratio. Here again is a number that varies over a relatively small range, so small a range, in fact, that in the interests of sensitivity, attention should be paid to at least the third decimal place. Almost all buildings have enclosure ratios falling between 1.5 and 4.5. Most ordinary structures will actually fall between 1.75 and 3.75. A one-story building with no interior walls, or partitions, only a roof and a floor, will have a ratio of 2.0. To produce ratios of less than this requires multistory construction; for example, a twenty-story building 100 ft square in plan, having a story height of 10 ft, would produce a ratio of 1.45, if it contained no interior partitions. Typical, reasonably efficient, high-rise apartment buildings usually have enclosure ratios of from 1.8 to 2.2. Residential buildings of other than these tend to have high enclosure ratios. This seems to be due to their high degree of interior space subdivision and the fact that the area of their roofs is divided over less floor area. One-story residence structures that are somewhat extended can be expected to have ratios of 4 to 4.5. A three-story office building having medium to large interior spaces would require a reasonably efficient configuration to produce an enclosure ratio of 2.75. If some degree of spatial freedom is due the architect, he should allow himself a ratio of at least 3.0 to solve any important architectural problem.

Aside from being something of an efficiency index and an aid to economic analysis, the floor area–enclosure ratio can be an aid to some extent in projecting other probable, quantitative effects of design variations. A cost assigned to a square foot of floor area by the procedure of multiplying the ratio by the estimated unit enclosure cost brings with it the accuracy inherent in the enclosure method of estimating, thereby eliminating the irrationality associated with floor-area estimating. If a program of design requirements establishes both the amount of floor area desired and a construction cost limitation, the architect can easily test the reasonableness of the given budget by determining that the ratio required to produce unit enclosure costs consistent with those for similar construction is feasible. He can do this far more accurately and simply by the use of the enclosure method than by any other. Another use that has been made of this figure is in the projection, prior to conception, of certain geometric characteristics of design schemes, thus establishing direction to the design effort with commensurate savings in trial-and-error work.

The more the architect works with enclosure quantities, the more familiar he becomes with this most significant property of buildings. As he develops a vocabulary of enclosure unit costs, enclosure–floor area ratios, and the like, the more accurately and quickly he can predict the outcome of his various efforts. In the long run, this will not be limited to predicting costs alone.

SEVEN

Gerald McKee, Jr.

Quantity Surveying
and Estimating

The term "quantity surveying" has three related meanings. The first refers to the practice of the British-chartered quantity surveyor and his counterparts in Sweden and elsewhere. In the United States, the term is employed to denote the procedures of measuring, counting, and analysis used in the preparation of a bill of construction material quantities. It is also used, in a rather imprecise way, to describe the practice of professional construction estimating in this country.

The quantity-survey system in England has been operative for more than 100 years, and its application is fundamental to the business of contracting there. In that country, a set of construction contract documents includes, in addition to the plans and specifications, a bill of quantities which defines the scope of the project for contract purposes. The preparation of this bill of quantities prior to the letting of a contract is the core effort of the quantity surveyor. In addition, his services have come to be used throughout the design and construction stages of most contracts.

He prepares budgets, administers cost control during design, reviews bids, evaluates modifications, etc. Since the bill of quantities is, in effect, the definition of contract responsibility, its preparation is undertaken with great care. Rules and procedures embodying pre-

103

cise standards of measurement and description are established by the Royal Institute of Chartered Surveyors. Computers are now in general use to assist in collecting, summarizing, and extending the material quantities.

The British practice of quantity surveying has several advantages. Since all contractors compute their bids from the contract bill of quantities, much costly duplication of effort is eliminated and many errors avoided. Most bids require that the bill be priced in detail by each contractor. Thus the contract becomes a very explicit cost document on which progress payments and change-order values can be based. Then too, this ensures that the entire construction process is carried out under the watchfulness of a cost-control program, administered by an equal but independent member of the team.

Despite its advantages, its long history, and the generally high esteem in which the quantity surveyor is held in Britain, the practice is increasingly criticized there. Primarily the critics feel that it is a restrictive and old-fashioned institution, more suited to brick-and-mortar construction than to the precast and curtain-wall features of modern buildings. In many areas of British influence, where the quantity-survey system was formerly employed, it is giving way to practices more akin to the American style of contracting.

Many efforts have been made in this country to launch a program of quantity surveying modeled on the British system. These have never been successful; the two methods of contracting are too disparate. American contractors, while recognizing the cost-saving aspects of an owner-furnished material takeoff are reluctant to place confidence in it as a basis for preparing bids. Then too, the absence of a universal language of construction, either for specifying or measuring, makes the prospects of adoption of a contracting system based on material quantities quite unlikely. U.S. contractors prefer to reserve for themselves or pass along to their subcontractors the responsibility for interpreting the requirements of the contract documents and for determining the materials and labor necessary to fulfill them.

In some parts of the United States, contractors, working through their trade organizations, have set up cooperative material-takeoff groups, thus cutting down the cost of bid preparation. These efforts are limited, however, both in number and in scope, and have, in any event, made no impact on the manner in which construction contracts are drawn.

There are, however, a great number of commercial firms throughout the country that furnish quantity surveys or bills of quantities from which contractors can prepare bids. These firms are usually somewhat small in size, very often one or two free-lance estimators, providing services to a following of contractors—and sometimes architects—who, because of either staff limitations or temporary overloads of work, prefer not to make their material takeoffs with in-house estimators. Many such quantity surveyors will sell a material quantity takeoff to several contractors bidding the same job. This further reduces the cost to an individual contractor using the service. Some of these quantity-survey groups will also "price" the estimate for the contractor, although this is usually to provide a check against the contractor's own efforts or those of his subcontractors.

Firms that provide a full estimating service—takeoff plus pricing—generally call themselves professional estimators or construction cost consultants and are likely to work for architects as frequently as for contractors. Furnishing estimates to architects introduces considerations which are quite distinct from those which apply to contractor estimating. For one thing, the scope of the effort is greatly expanded. The general contractor will probably want estimates for only those building trades he proposes to furnish himself, usually quite few in number, while the architect will more likely be concerned with the cost of the entire building.

The second difference between estimating for architects and for contractors, and perhaps the more critical one, arises from the need of the architect to obtain cost information before contract drawings are complete. The architect's estimator must be able to work from incomplete working drawings, preliminary drawings, sketches, and even project descriptions.

These two considerations—the number of trades to be estimated and the need for working from an incomplete design—require that the professional estimator who services architects have a more diversified background than the contractor's quantity surveyor. Generally, it means that the organization providing these services will be larger, and will employ estimators drawn from various construction experiences.

The services provided to architects by estimating firms vary greatly, of course, in accordance with the architect's needs. A full program of cost control from earliest design through award of the construction contract may include estimates at the budget, preliminary, and contract stages of architectural services and during construction.

Budget Estimate

This is a joint effort with the architect to determine the major cost features of a proposed project. While architects very often establish budget estimates on a basis of gross square feet of building area, procedures of much greater sensitivity are available. An experienced estimator can develop, during an interview or with the help of a specially prepared questionnaire, a description of the project detailed sufficiently to permit establishment of a reliable, realistic budget. Perhaps the pro-

fessional estimator may be expected to be more objective than the architect at this stage, since he may more easily avoid the optimism, which
so often pervades the establishment of a project budget, of owner and
architect regarding the ultimate project cost.

Preliminary Estimate

This is an estimate prepared from the architect's definitive preliminary
drawings and outline specifications. Ideally, the design concept is fixed
at this point, and most decisions involving cost have been made. The
professional estimator may then, if he has accumulated the requisite
skills and cost data, prepare an estimate in considerable detail. Principal
building features and components of major systems can be analyzed
at this stage. A preliminary estimate, properly prepared, will be a dis-
cursive statement of cost. It will not only provide a check on the budget
but also show how the cost is distributed throughout the building. Only
in this way may the kinds of discussions and decisions that characterize
an owner's review of preliminary documents be soundly based on building values. If the project cost has crept above the budget, a reduction
program can be carried out with some assurance that goals will be
met without unnecessary sacrifice.

Contract Estimate

This is an estimate which is prepared from complete or nearly complete contract drawings. It serves as a final check on the budget and
provides much information that is valuable in bid review, approval of
progress payment schedules, and evaluation of contract modifications.

Change Orders and Claims

Many architects continue the services of a professional estimator
through the actual construction program. He may be employed to estimate the cost of proposed modifications, to evaluate the contractor's
change-order proposals, and to negotiate them to an equitable settlement. The fact that the estimating consultant keeps himself current with
the hard facts of construction costs and practice and the fact that his
staff is drawn largely from the building trades make his contribution
here a valuable one.

When a full cost-control program is undertaken, the cost consultant
very often provides a variety of supplementary services—comparative
cost analyses, market studies, etc. Properly administered, such a cost-control program is quite fluid and provides what amounts to a continuous
review of the project-cost features and their relation to the budget.

It is axiomatic that project costs will be increased during the preparation of working drawings unless strict controls are applied.

In part to seek objectivity, and in part because of a growing recognition that an intensive cost-control program lies outside the scope of the architect's traditional service (and fee), more and more owners are being persuaded to treat the cost-consultant's charges as an owner-reimbursed cost.

Such charges are not insignificant. If he engages a first-rate estimating consultant, the architect can expect to spend 5 percent of his fee for a full program of cost control (exclusive of change-order evaluation), as outlined above. For a project of 1 million dollars construction value, of average complexity, this would be perhaps $3,000 for a full estimating program. For such a fee the architect is entitled to, and should demand, the same depth of experience, expertise, and cooperation he expects from his other consultants. In engaging a professional estimator or construction-cost consultant, the architect should make sure that certain criteria are met, if he intends to get full value for the fee paid. Ideally, the estimating firm selected should be able to estimate all or virtually all trades (including mechanical trades when required) with members of his own permanent staff. While estimators from construction companies are readily available for "moonlighting" assignments, responsible estimating firms avoid using them. Such men, even when highly talented, seldom have the requisite background for preparing budget or preliminary estimates and cannot, in any event, assure primacy of interest and continued availability throughout the life of a project.

Of course, the experience of the firm is quite important. An organization that prepares estimates primarily for contractors is not likely to have developed either the skills or the cost data necessary for budget and preliminary estimating. Estimating for contractors is very much a matter of measuring, counting, analyzing—in short, estimating what can be seen on the construction drawings. Estimating for architects requires the additional ability to evaluate what has not yet been rendered explicit in plan or specification. A brief visit to the estimator's office, followed by a careful inquiry into work he has performed for other architects, will probably provide the best means for evaluating his service.

If an architect proposes to take full advantage of his use of a professional estimating firm, he must consider that group a full-fledged part of his design team. The estimator evaluates information he gets from the architect, and nothing more; thus the flow of information must be full and responsive. A good cost consultant will know what information he needs and how to get it, with the least disruption to the architect's production efforts. He will need the architect's cooperation, however, and the architect's support in soliciting data from other design consultants.

EIGHT

Allen E. Cox

Value Engineering

Architecture was cognizant of value engineering long before industry was even aware that a need for it existed. In 1756, the Italian Carlo Lodali said, "In architecture only that shall show that has a definite function, and which derives from the strictest necessity." Louis Sullivan, writing in *Lippincott's Magazine* in 1896, said, "Over all the coursing sun, form ever follows function, and this is the law." Both statements are particularly apropos, since the foundation of value engineering is functional analysis.

"Value" is defined as "the least cost to accomplish the function." From this, "value engineering" then becomes "the identification of unnecessary cost." The terms value engineering and value analysis are used almost interchangeably by many. Strictly speaking, however, value analysis usually refers to identification of unnecessary cost in products already in production, a term somewhat meaningless in our field.

Industrially speaking, the need for value engineering came about because products were designed to "work" and because many shop practices were based solely on "good engineering," neither of these German land mines during World War II were turned brass pins about ⅛ in. in diameter with turned heads. When the mine was armed, this pin was extracted and thrown away. "Good German engineering" perhaps, but a piece of soft wire accomplished the function in the U.S. mines at much less cost.

At the end of World War II, Lawrence D. Miles at General Electric discovered that often substitutions, dictated by shortages, resulted in products that accomplished their function at reduced cost. He set out to formalize this process, with the emphasis on costs, and thus value engineering was born.

Although born in industry, the techniques of value engineering are pertinent to any field where unnecessary costs exist. By definition this would then include construction which utilizes practices and procedures contributing to unnecessary cost; value engineering can ferret them out.

To go back and amplify our original definition of VE, we might say that value engineering, by means of an organized group approach and following a formalized job plan, identifies unnecessary cost. The group approach is basic for two reasons. In industry, bringing in someone from another department results in a new and different look at the problem. Also, the more departments represented, the easier it will be to "sell" the proposed changes to the appropriate authority. Ideally, the VE team is made up of people from purchasing, engineering, and production, headed by a VE specialist. In the case of an architect's office, a team might be made up of people with different specialties including, additionally, field men, specification writers, administrative people, perhaps representatives of specialty vendors and subcontractors, and, ideally, construction management. The broadest possible base, regardless of technical competence in the specific field of the problem, is the objective.

The team proceeds with the job plan. Mr. Miles of GE prefers a seven-phase plan; however, many practitioners prefer a somewhat simpler and more descriptive plan which we shall refer to as the "five what's":

1. What is it?
2. What does it do?
3. What does it cost?
4. What else will do it?
5. What will that cost?

This, in essence, is what value engineering is all about. However, unless dealing with exceptionally creative people, considerable training is required to satisfactorily utilize even as simple a plan as that above. The job plan proceeds as follows.

Under the first step, all pertinent data are accumulated. Included are such things as all specifications governing the construction or fabrication of the item being analyzed, all performance requirements, all costs, all drawings, and anything else having a bearing on the item in question. Here, all means exactly that, nothing less. For example, such things as standard specs and general contract provisions must be included if they may in any way affect the cost of the item in question.

In the second step, a functional analysis is performed. This is essential. The function of each component must be defined in two words, a verb and a noun, as must the function of the whole. The accompanying table shows how this might be accomplished for an object with which we are all familiar: the incandescent light bulb. It will be noted that the basic function of the bulb is "provide light" and only one component, the filament, fulfills this function; all other components fulfill secondary functions. The analyst making up this particular example apparently felt that he had a good chance of reducing the filament cost. Since that time, one of the photoflash manufacturers has made even bigger savings by removing the base and conducting current through two wires extending from the glass.

Functional Analysis Form

Product: Light Bulb
Basic Function: Provide Light

Part description	Quantity function		Degree		Costs	
	Verb	Noun	Basic	Second-ary	Target	Pres-ent
Glass Bulb	Excludes	Air		X		3¢
Base	Supports	Lamp		X		8¢
	Conducts	Current				
Stem	Supports	Leads		X		1¢
Filament	Provides	Light	X		3¢	5¢
Supports (filament)	Support	Filament		X		½¢
Contact	Conducts	Current		X		1¢
Lead Wires	Conducts	Current		X		2¢
Cement	Excludes	Air		X		½¢
Insulator (base)	Blocks	Current		X		¼¢
Gas (inert)	Prevents	Oxidation		X		1¢
Ink (trademark)	Provides	Identification		X		½¢
Solder	Provides	Contact		X		¼¢
Exhaust Tube	Conducts	Air		X		1¢
Total						24¢

Once the functional analysis is performed, costs must be assigned to each and every function, as in the light bulb example. Included with these functions will very often be "sell" functions or "aesthetic" functions. For example, the chrome plating on an automobile door handle fulfills the basic function, "prevents rusting," but its secondary function is 'improves appearance." The cost of the basic function would be the cost of painting the door handle. The cost of the secondary function would be the difference between the cost of painting and chroming. It is often surprising to discover how much of the cost of anything is devoted to sell functions. For example, in residential construction, the built-in appliances are not that much more efficient than separate appliances and, in fact, create some difficulties in servicing and replacement. The big reason for their popularity is that they fulfill a sell function for the house.

At this point, although it is not a separate step, the question should be asked, "What is in (the function) worth?" For example, in the analysis of an apartment building, we might find several hundred coat hooks in the closets. The basic function of these hooks is "support clothing." The worth of the function would be the cost of driving a large nail in place of each hook. This would fulfill the basic function at a fraction of the cost. It would also provide a target for maximum possible savings. Ridiculous? Perhaps, but this act of determining worth is very important from another aspect. It breaks away from the usual solution and gets the team warmed up for the creative process.

"What else will do it?" is the creative phase of the job plan. During this phase, all of the known tools of creative problem solving are used. Brainstorming, talking to specialty vendors and specialty contractors, and anything else that will inject fresh thinking and a fresh approach are used. At this stage, if not before, every specification and every method must be questioned. It is also at this stage that the value of team members from outside the pertinent discipline becomes apparent. When one team member says, "We can't do that," perhaps another says, "Why not?" Sometimes it develops that there is no reason except custom.

The whole value-engineering concept hinges on the creative phase, and a good share of VE training time is devoted to it. Actually, we are not too certain that people can be trained to be creative, in spite of many tests and published results. We are, however, certain that most people use only a small amount of their inherent, creative potential. This potential can be realized through training. This training usually takes the form of trying to break people out of their behavioral ruts. An example might be, "How many uses can you think of for the common, yellow, rubber-tipped, wooden pencil?" A group of six people one evening came up with well over two hundred in approximately the time needed by one person to write them down.

Once alternatives are developed, it only remains to get costs on them and select the one desired. Ideally, this is the one costing the least; circumstances, of course, sometimes dictate otherwise.

Perhaps here a word of warning is in order. There are traps in the value-engineering field that one should beware of.

The first of these is that, unfortunately, value engineering is always a threat to someone. Because designs originate with someone else, the value engineer is always second-guessing. Very often his proposed changes look ridiculously simple—after they are proposed.

Another trap is the temptation among some practitioners in the field to reduce the whole thing to a formula with charts and nomograms, a paradox in itself, inasmuch as one of the prime targets of value engineering is the repeated use of the same formulas.

A third trap is the fact that one man's standard may be another's special. It is common in value-analysis work to substitute a standard component in one field or a special in another. For example, plastic caps and plugs, which were used originally to plug openings in hydraulic components against dirt, are now used as a substitute for a variety of special-order caps and plugs in the electronics, missile, and aircraft industries. On the other hand, in construction, the standards are often a trap. To take a simple example, does the standard manhole cover and ring, or the standard catch basin grating, represent the lowest cost to accomplish the function? Perhaps, but has anyone ever checked?

In the industrial or hardware field, savings have been realized in the most astounding places. Lockheed-Georgia, for example, required four standard foam fire trucks for C-141 aircraft fire-suppression capability at a cost of $703,000. A VE effort led them to develop a single giant truck at $230,000—a saving of $465,000 in labor and equipment. At the other end of the scale, the Boeing Company reduced the number of standard fastener, hold, drill, reamer, and bushing sizes by 50 percent for a resulting saving of $410,000 per year.

Savings in commercial industry are harder to document for competitive reasons. However, one of the major manufacturers of mining machinery turned a money-losing conveyor, which they were manufacturing only to provide a complete line, into their best money maker. The Hoover Company credits value engineering with cutting $20 off the retail price of their vacuum cleaners over the last four years.

Does this hardware approach have anything to do with construction? Certainly. Unnecessary costs need identification in construction just as much as anywhere else. Once one begins to examine the function, one finds myriad examples of unnecessary cost.

As an example of what is being done, the Navy's Bureau of Yards and Docks realized savings averaging $1,000 per unit in one of their housing projects by value engineering their standard plans. They substituted paint-grade plywood or metal for prefinished birch kitchen cabinets; they substituted pit-run gravel for crushed stone under the concrete floor slabs; they removed the vapor barrier under the floor slab, since water was no problem at the particular location analyzed; they eliminated soil poisoning and preservation of first-floor studs when they found termites were no problem locally; they eliminated reinforcing bars in the foundation wall; they redesigned the roof truss for less material; they substituted prefab stairs for site-built stairs, and similar items of a lesser nature.

At the other end of the scale, the Corps of Engineers reports savings of over 3 million dollars by changing the design of a lock wall from a gravity section to a massive head buttress. This design not only saved concrete costs, but reduced hydraulic uplift, which was a problem in that particular location.

We've looked at the techniques and we've looked at what is being done. What can be done in the future to reduce construction costs? Without knowing the specific project, it is hard to say, but there certainly are general areas at which the VE team should take a long, hard look.

In the area of substructures, cleaning and preparation should be examined carefully to determine if they fulfill a basic function. Mass concrete should be looked at carefully to avoid unnecessary costs that will not contribute to function. Overdesign because of inspection difficulty can be reduced. Cameras and closed circuit TV can inspect where a man cannot, at less cost than overdesign due to unknown factors.

When it comes to superstructures, more welding should be used where it will reduce costs. Many architects avoid welding because of unfamiliarity and difficulty of inspection, yet missiles, aircraft, automobiles, and ships are all welded with a great deal of success. A modern quality-control program with statistical sampling could decrease the cost of weld inspection tremendously and at no more risk than the program used in jet aircraft. The triangle, as opposed to the rectangle, should be examined as a structural system. Utilization of various grades of steel in the same structure should be increased so that the minimum amount of cost is devoted to carrying the weight of the structure itself. Functions should be combined where money can be saved, an example being T-slab construction which combines the floor slab and beam in one unit. Composite construction is another step in this direction. To carry this a step further, a recent composite ridge deck had beams spaced so that standard plywood sheets would fit between the webs without cutting. Simple blocking on the bottom flanges supported these plywood deck forms. To go back to our functional analysis, the basic function of the bottom flange is "resists tension." However, in this case it fulfills a secondary function, "supports forms."

The subject of structural exteriors raises some particularly thorny problems when it comes to value engineering a project. If the function of the exterior treatment is "improves appearance," "provides texture," "provides color," etc., then properly speaking it fulfills a sell or aesthetic function. It then becomes a matter of how much an owner is willing to pay for this. On the other hand, if the exterior treatment fulfills some function, such as "prevents corrosion" or "prevents decay," then some progress can be made toward improving value. For example, the type of alloy steel which has been used on several bridges and buildings and which forms its own protective oxide coating, thereby needing no paint, can be used. Another example is a recently developed sulfur and glass-fiber coating for concrete block that bonds the blocks together after they have been stacked dry. It also provides a hard, impervious surface, another example of providing more than the function.

Unfortunately, all the case examples and suggestions in the world will not make a value-engineering program. Value engineering is as much a state of mind as it is an art or skill. One must constantly be aware of the five what's of the job plan in every aspect of one's work. It is amazing how many useless things and activities one discovers if constantly asking oneself "What is the function?" To take a simple example, acoustical tile:

What is it? It is the visible surface of a ceiling, often made of wood fibers, usually with a decorative pattern of holes in it, probably in 1-ft squares stapled to furring strips or glued to the ceiling.

What does it do? Its basic function is "deadens sound." Its secondary functions are "provides surface" and "provides decoration."

What does it cost? The material costs approximately 20¢ per sq ft plus 2¢ per sq ft for flame proofing.

What else will do it? Here there are lots of answers, depending on the creativity and ingenuity of the VE team, although 90 percent of the list probably will seem ridiculous at first glance. The one finally selected, in one case: papier-mâché layer dividers from egg crates.

What will that cost? 2½¢ per sq ft for materials plus 2¢ for flame proofing.

Savings—$175 per thousand sq ft of ceiling or approximately 40 percent of the installed price. Worth going after?

So far, we've discussed all the benefits of value engineering. Are these benefits obtainable at no cost? No, they are not. Everything of value costs something.

To begin with, the hardware-oriented defense industries which have value-engineering programs find that the ratio of savings realized to program cost is about 7 to 1. Unfortunately, since the technique is new in the construction field, there are no reliable statistics as yet to shoot at.

In regard to program costs, two things ought to be mentioned. First is that trained VE people are currently in short supply. The total membership of SAVE (Society of American Value Engineers) is approximately 2,500. The second thing to keep in mind is that there are training costs involved for you and your people.

Let us examine three possible ways to get started on a VE program. These are listed in decreasing order of cost.

The first is to hire an outside consultant to train your people and head up your program. The customary form of VE training is the workshop seminar of thirty-five to forty hours duration. This can train from thirty to fifty people simultaneously. Since these usually involve teams of from three to six people and since each team works on a project from their own firm or department, these seminars customarily return savings that more than equal the cost of the training. The cost of such a seminar would be approximately $7,500. The fee for consultation on a regular basis varies, as do all consulting fees, but $150 per day plus expenses would probably be a fair average. A variation of this approach is to hire a full-time value engineer from industry to head up a permanent program. A competent man could be obtained at a cost of $15,000 to $20,000 per year. He would start by holding training sessions and then head up the program.

The next way to start is to train a smaller group of your own people in a public or semipublic seminar and then rely on them to conduct a program without further aid. This might not be quite as effective as the first method, but would cost considerably less. These seminars can be obtained in a variety of ways. In New England, for example, Northeastern University regularly holds evening VE seminars. Several of the technical societies sponsor evening seminars. The Worcester Area Chamber of Commerce holds an annual evening seminar, at which the writer has instructed, every spring. Certainly these same activities go on in other regions. Additionally, institutions such as the University of Wisconsin offer a summer course in value engineering; not to be overlooked are the University of Buffalo's summer creativity seminars, which are very popular with value engineers. To get back to evening seminars, the cost of such seminars is nominal inasmuch as the instructor is usually a practicing, local value engineer instructing on a part-time basis. A cost of $75 to $100 per man should cover this type of training. Once your people are trained, the only cost for the program is the cost of the time they spend devoted to value engineering. Should you not know of any training being given in your area, the nearest chapter or national headquarters of SAVE should be able to put you in touch with competent instructors who will instruct a sponsored course for a nominal fee.

The third approach is the individual program. It would probably be necessary to travel to some location where a public seminar was being held. Once trained, one could then conduct one's own program. This is admittedly the least effective because of the absence of a team but should not be overlooked nonetheless. In the first place, the training is of value to any creative person. Secondly, if handled properly, savings can be made. For an individual program, it is suggested that designs be made much as usual. Then the designer's hat is removed and the value engineer's hat donned and a value analysis performed. From actual experience, this technique has been found surprisingly effective.

We have examined the subject of value engineering as thoroughly as space will permit. The attitude of the architect may now be "this is very interesting but . . ." The author, as a professional engineer, is quite aware of the obligations already shouldered by architects and engineers to provide the best, most economical design they know how. However, you will find that with the new slant given you by VE training, you will come up with savings you never thought possible. This is particularly true if you will let it make you look at your work from a different vantage point, or outside yourself as it were. After all, much of the architecture that we consider great today resulted from the architect's stepping outside himself and taking a new approach to his problem.

How will value engineering enable you to save money for your client? The easiest way is to establish a program to review designs in-house. You will find that savings will be made constantly. The only cautionary note is to make sure that the principals in your firm are behind the program all the way, because it is going to threaten some of your people personally.

The second way is to put a VE incentive clause in contracts between owner and contractor. This would be similar to the clauses used by the Department of Defense wherein the contractor shares savings, developed through value engineering, with the owner, usually on a 50-50 basis. This approach is really sticking your neck out and asking to have it chopped. It means, in essence, that the contractors are always going to be sniping at your designs and second-guessing you. All you have to gain is the reputation of being able to bring a project in at less cost than anyone else.

In order to make the VE processes, as applied to architecture, as clear as possible in a limited space, it might be well to end with a considerably simplified set of notes on the application of VE to a basic, very simple building.

Notes on Value Engineering a Simple Building

To begin with, let us keep in mind our five basic questions of value engineering:

What is it? What does it do? What does it cost? What else will do it? What will that cost?

These questions should be asked regarding every component of the structure.

Suppose we start with a simple, small, industrial warehouse to store bagged chemicals on pallets stacked 12 ft high. Let's say it is 50 ft wide by 100 ft long. The floor is concrete. There are doors at each end, windows at regular intervals along the side walls. To keep the problem simple, we'll further specify that climate control is not required.

Let's start with a functional analysis (What does it do?). The basic function of the building is "enclose space." The functions of the parts are as follows:

Part	Basic function	Secondary function
Footings	Support walls	Resist thrust
Floor	Supports contents	Supports vehicles
Walls	Enclose space	Resist wind
Columns	Support roof	Support walls
Doors	Permit entrance	Provide ventilation
Windows	Provide light	Provide ventilation
Roof	Encloses space	Supports snow
Lights	Provide illumination	

The first impulse might be to design the building with a column and truss skeleton, with either a pitched roof and light roofing or a flat roof with built-up roofing. Walls could then be steel sheet or precast-concrete panels. But, there are some fallacies in this decision.

The basic function of the truss is "support roof," the secondary function is "connect columns." But, what is the point of the truss supporting the roof all by itself? Since there will be racks for pallets all through the interior, why not have small columns among the racks? A column-free interior in this case fulfills no function; providing columns greatly simplifies roof framing and results in decreased cost.

Now, let us carry this thought one step further. The basic function of the original exterior columns was "support roof." Suppose we support the roof on the pallet racks we are going to install anyway. This will save the cost of exterior columns.

Let's take a look at the substructure. Are concrete footings really necessary? Unless a local code requires them, probably the whole structure could be floated on the floor slab. We'll assume that the floor is a 6-in. slab of reinforced concrete. Its basic function is "supports contents." But, what about the area where there are no contents to support? At these locations, all that is necessary is a dirt seal. Several approaches should be investigated here. One might be precast footings for the racks with sand and gravel filled partway up in the no-load areas and then the no-load areas and the aisles filled with poured-in-place concrete. Another approach might be a complete poured-in-place slab with cardboard tubes or even boxes providing voids in the no-load areas. A couple of other items to watch here are the strength of the concrete and anchor bolts. There is no reason why there should be 3,500 psi concrete in no-load areas. Anchorages should be value analyzed to make sure they fulfill a function; complicated anchorages add to the cost of concrete.

The problems mentioned in the preceding paragraph should be brainstormed by a group under the "What else will do it?" heading. For example, why do we have to stick to concrete? Maybe a sheet of plywood in the no-load areas would provide a satisfactory solution. Parenthetically, this should also be applied to the pallet racks. For example, maybe the uprights could be precast, prestressed concrete columns.

To go on, let us look at the walls. These should be made of whatever material will provide the required durability to resist the elements over the required period of time and of sufficient strength to resist the wind load. Here again, the VE teams should examine all possible alternatives. I can visualize alternatives ranging from plastic sheets, through paper, cardboard, and plywood to precast concrete. It must be kept in mind that the basic function of the walls is "enclose space" with the secondary function, "resist wind"; they have no other functions. For example, insulation value is of no importance, structural strength is of very little importance, and so on.

The roof is pretty cut and dried. Some savings have already been made by having the racks support the roof. This involves multiple support and therefore requires less structural strength in the roof. From here on, whatever will provide the functions of the roof at the least cost is the thing to pick.

Remaining we have doors, windows, and lights. A few remarks are in order here. The first impulse is to have a door at each end big enough for a truck or a forklift, depending on requirements. But, does the second door fulfill a function? Quite possibly not. Secondly, there are many varieties of door on the market at a variety of prices. Perhaps a plain barn door on a track might fulfill the function at the lowest cost. Do the windows fulfill a necessary function? Doubtful, since they will be blocked to a large extent by racks. Since lighting is provided anyway, I would omit the windows. Under the heading of lighting, I can see only two things to watch: keep the runs of wire and number of units to a minimum, and avoid the temptation to light the warehouse up like a precision-assembly area.

To carry the whole thing a step further, although perhaps not usually within the realm of most architects, we should question the necessity for bags, pallets, pallet racks, and forklift. Depending on the owner's situation, it would be less costly to handle this material in bulk. We could then go to a modified A-frame of steel or plywood, storing the material on the floor and sloping the walls to match the angle of repose.

NINE

James J. O'Brien

Critical Path
Method

Critical Path Method (CPM) can be a significant factor in cost control. The method was developed in 1957 and 1958 to utilize electronic computers for construction scheduling. Subsequent to this development, CPM has been utilized independently of the computer, and the computer has been relegated to its proper place of support for the CPM system. The real strength of CPM is its basis in common logic.

Construction scheduling until the advent of CPM (and its similar aerospace system PERT) was based upon the Gantt chart or bargraph. The strength of the bar graph is in its excellent visual presentation of a schedule. However, the planning features which went into the makeup of that schedule are not demonstrated on the bar graph. In Fig. 9.1, the ease with which a bar graph can be manipulated without reference to the planning logic is demonstrated.

The strength and simplicity of the basic CPM approach is so obvious after a successful application has been made that the originators of the system anticipated that the entire construction industry would be on a CPM basis in the early 1960s. They reckoned without the inertia of the status quo. CPM is utilized on only about 10 to 20 percent of the construction currently in progress. Among

119

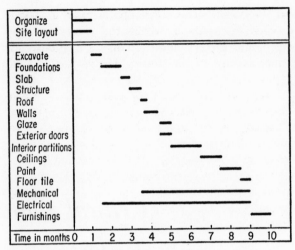

FIG. 9.1 *Bar chart, small office building. (From
James J. O'Brien, "CPM in Construction Manage-
ment," McGraw-Hill Book Company, New York, 1965.
By permission of the publishers.)*

architects and engineers, about 20 percent have utilized CPM/PERT,
and another 20 percent expect to. Usage will continue to grow, and the
cost-control advantages should increase as the application broadens.

Cost Phases

CPM project application has three specific cost application areas:

1. *Construction Phase* The most advantageous area of CPM application is during the construction phase. This is also the usual application
area and is often considered to be the complete CPM application.

2. *Design Phase* CPM can be applied in two manners during the
design phase. First, it can be used to plan the design phase itself. Secondly, it can be used to prepare a prebid construction CPM to establish
a reasonable construction schedule.

3. *Budgetary Phase* CPM can be utilized during the early predesign
budgetary phase to plan major capital programs. CPMs in this area
can be very effective.

Construction Phase

CPM and non-CPM plans may be identical. But with CPM to develop
foresight, the plan is applied before troubles develop rather than as
a reflex to the unexpected.

Time is money in construction. The contractor saves overhead money in a shorter project, and the owner saves substantially more in having the use of the facility when he needs it. While the contractor does save money in a CPM-program project, these savings are usually less than the value of the time savings to the owner. The owner also has an incentive to plan and implement the schedule, carefully, with the objective of shortening it; however, the contractor also usually has concurrent projects which might furnish greater savings per unit of resource. Accordingly, the owner cannot depend solely upon the contractor's advantage in project schedule maintenance. Also, it is almost axiomatic that there are fewer extras on a fast-moving, well-coordinated project. Accordingly, while the contractor gains through CPM, the owner's project gains much more. It is therefore often to the owner's advantage to furnish or underwrite the cost of CPM planning if the contractor does not normally furnish it.

Advantages of CPM

If the various benefits of CPM had to be expressed in three words, they would be planning, discipline, and communication.

Planning CPM is not in itself a plan. It is a method of demonstrating and evaluating the plans which were developed by the construction team. This is a significant concept, because much of the resistance to CPM is based upon the reluctance to let a computer plan for the project. The fact is that the CPM plan *must* represent the plan which the contractor expects to follow in the field. Anything else is academic. However, in translating the contractor's plan into CPM, the opportunity is presented to record in detail the planning ideas in a manner not previously possible. CPM permits planning in detail and sharp focus on the area under consideration. The advantages are that the planner does not have to hold the entire project in his mind simultaneously but can concentrate on areas as their sequence is developed. In a construction survey, contractors noted the following planning advantages:

1. Makes you think out plans beforehand.
2. Shows each step of the job.
3. Diagrams add realism to scheduling.

Discipline Preparation of the CPM diagram forces planning because lack of decisions will result in gaps in the diagrams. CPM forces the planner to put down his best available information now rather than waiting, perhaps too long, for final information. During the course of the project, the regular review of the CPM plan and schedule furnishes a positive discipline review on a specific basis. CPM then offers a framework against which the traditional job meetings add a new dimension of evaluation.

Communication The CPM plan presents planning factors in a logically connected fashion at the earliest practical point in the project. This permits constructive critique of the planning factors in a manner not previously possible. Also, the level of communication which is realized in the preparation of the network can be very effective. Group planning sessions are very desirable. In a conference approach for a refinery turn-around, the contractor was impassive as the plan was discussed. At one point, he noted that the project could be planned any way at all on the blackboard, but he would have his way in the field. We convinced him that it was his own plan that was desired, and he entered the CPM preparation. The results were rapid. In a major boiler renovation, elaborate A-frame supports were to be prefabricated. The contractor described why he would not be able to utilize these supports, and the direct and inexpensive (and safe) method of temporary support for the headers which he intended to use. His method was accepted immediately, and the expensive prefabrication was avoided.

Network Form

The size of the CPM network is generally a function of the manner in which the contractor intends to use the plan, and also the reasons for his using it. If CPM has been specified, and the contractor does not normally utilize it, his approach is often to provide a minimum CPM scope. This in itself is not necessarily a poor approach. A good outline-type network can be very useful even if the contractor does not utilize it to its fullest advantage.

Although network size does not equate to network quality, if CPM is specified, a useful guideline is the number of activities to be included. Early CPM networks were often in the 200 to 300 activity range for major projects. The same holds true today for many contractor-furnished networks. Where the contractor is used to using CPM, or the owner is furnishing a full CPM service, network size often runs 1,000 to 3,000 activities. The design network alone for the TVA Bullrun Dam involved more than 12,000 activities.

The cost per activity is also a method of controlling the network size. There is however no definite value which should be assigned to each arrow. The extreme limitations are obvious. An arrow should certainly represent more than a few dollars, and a single arrow should not represent several hundred thousand dollars. However, the exact limitations within these extremes is difficult to set arbitrarily. Generally, no arrow (except material deliveries) should cover a period of more than two weeks. In meeting the letter of this rule, one contractor broke the spirit of it by showing fourteen weeks of conduit installations in seven two-week increments as follows:

Place Conduit	Place Conduit	Place Conduit	Place Conduit	Place Conduit	Place Conduit	Place Conduit
⟶	⟶	⟶	⟶	⟶	⟶	⟶
10 days	10 days	10 days	10 days	10 days	10 days	10 days

Planners' Outlook

The CPM plan will be the contractor's. For any project a wide range of CPM results could be anticipated. The best situation is a well-qualified contractor who has made a good bid and has good CPM experience. Many contractors have used CPM well in this type of situation. However, even where a company has a good reputation, the final results depend very much upon the individual situation including all cognizant members of the construction team in particular, the superintendent, the owner, and the architect.

Even when the contractor prepares an excellent CPM plan, he necessarily views the project in terms of his own situation rather than in terms of the needs of the owner. Where the CPM plan is contractor-prepared, the owner has no control over its completeness, quality accuracy, or maintenance. The best results to date have been realized where the owner, often through a consultant, the architect, or both, furnishes the CPM plan preparation to the contractor. This requires a professional attitude on the part of the CPM planner to work in a fair and objective manner. This objective approach is of value to all of the prime participants in the project. In this objective CPM application, there will be occasions when the owner or the architect becomes the critical factor in job progress. However, to be effective, CPM or any planning must be realistic and look at the true factors involved. CPM can be used as a hammer and has been in a few cases. The use of CPM to develop a truly cooperative effort is a much more significant approach.

Auxiliary Areas

The basic CPM plan is made up of the work activities in the field. However, when the diagram is to be used to effectively plan and control progress for the project, the availability of materials and equipment as needed is a very important consideration. These activities representing material ordering, shop drawing preparation and approval, and delivery times are superimposed upon the basic CPM plan for the project. The level of detail used should be a function of and directly proportional

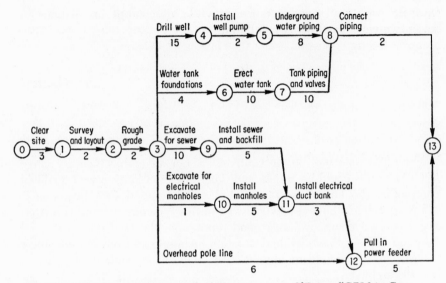

FIG. 9.2 *Site preparation network. (From James J. O'Brien, "CPM in Construction Management," McGraw-Hill Book Company, New York, 1965. By permission of the publishers.)*

to the expected utilization of the information. With a contractor experienced in the application of CPM, the level of detail would usually be substantially greater than the outline detail for monitoring alone.

Figure 9.2 shows a simple CPM plan for site-preparation phase of a small project. Figures 9.3 and 9.4 show the material procurement network which would be superimposed upon Fig. 9.2 to tie in the procurement cycle. Note that the procurement cycle varies with the type of equipment or material to be purchased. Some are catalog items, others require an architect's full review. Note that the addition of these twenty-four procurement activities has more than doubled the size of the original seventeen-activity network. Nevertheless, material availability often determines progress of the job. Also, architect's approval of shop drawings is now in the schedule, and delays in this area can be avoided. The CPM calculation gives an indication of priority required for the procurement cycle. This is a function both of the point in the project at which the item is required and the sum of the procurement times involved. Another important value of the inclusion of material deliveries in the CPM plan is a disciplined procedural check upon the procurement cycle. Many of the material problems which occur on a project are the result of omissions or mistakes in ordering. On a major New York City apartment house, one month was lost through the failure to order door bucks early in the project. The contractor recognized the importance of the early ordering of these door bucks; the error occurred through omission rather than lack of knowledge.

Computation

Figure 9.5 shows the event-time calculations for the CPM network shown in Fig. 9.2. In this case, the calculation was done manually. The CPM calculation is no more than the determination of the longest path through the network, which in this case is through events 0-1-2-3-4-5-8-13. The difference between the longest or critical path and the length of other paths is called float. The more difference or flexibility, the greater the float or slack.

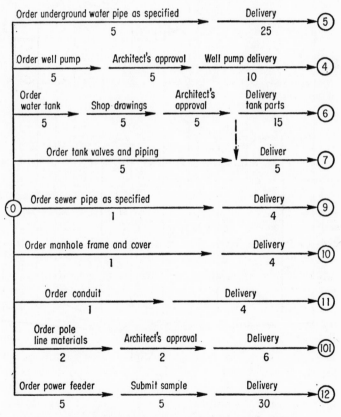

FIG. 9.3 *Material procurement cycle, site work. (From James J. O'Brien, "CPM in Construction Management," McGraw-Hill Book Company, New York, 1965. By permission of the publishers.)*

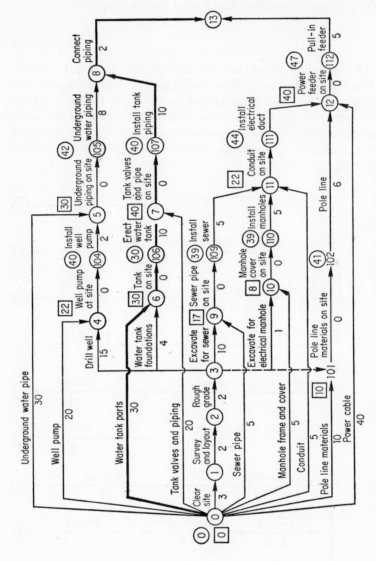

FIG. 9.4 *Deliveries for site preparation, zero delivery times. (From James J. O'Brien, "CPM in Construction Management," McGraw-Hill Book Company, New York, 1965. By permission of the publishers.)*

The decision on whether to use a manual calculation or a computer is generally a function of the size and complexity of the network. There is no single size break point. Generally, however, a network of less than 250 activities can be hand-calculated more rapidly than it can be introduced into the computer. However, if regular updating of the network is expected, computer computation of a network as small as 100 activities may be practical. On larger networks, the computer saves both time and money. It should be recognized that the computer performs no mystical operations and makes no decisions in the course of the CPM calculation. The computer calculation is very similar to the manual calculation shown in Fig. 9.5.

When a computer is to be used, the first consideration may be where to find one. There are at least twenty types of computers which can run CPM networks. In a CPM survey, 55 percent of the group surveyed indicated that they either have a computer available or can get one. If an in-house computer is not available, service center equipment is probably convenient to the project location. Computer programs for CPM are readily available, although these can vary in efficiency and running time. The IBM Basic Less Program still remains one of the fundamental programs for CPM.

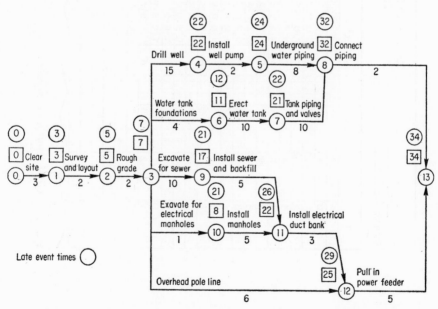

FIG. 9.5 *Late event times, site preparation. (From James J. O'Brien, "CPM in Construction Management," McGraw-Hill Book Company, New York, 1965. By permission of the publishers.)*

Client JOHN DOE
Contract No. 315

Critical - Path Planning & Scheduling
Data Layout

Page 1 of 1
Date

I (1–4)	J (5–8)	Time duration (9–12)	13–17	Job Description (18–44)
0	1	3	11	CLEAR SITE
1	2	2	12	SURVEY & LAYOUT
2	3	2	11	ROUGH GRADE
3	4	15	17	DRILL WELL
3	6	4	13	WATER TANK FOUNDATIONS
3	9	10	11	EXCAVATE FOR SEWER
3	10	1	11	EXCAVATE ELECTRICAL MANHOLE
3	12	6	14	OVERHEAD POLE LINE
4	5	2	15	INSTALL WELL PUMP
5	8	8	15	UNDERGROUND WATER PIPING
6	7	10	16	ERECT WATER TOWER
7	8	10	15	TANK PIPING AND VALVES
8	13	2	15	CONNECT WATER PIPING
9	11	5	15	INSTALL SEWER AND BACKFILL
10	11	5	14	INSTALL ELECTRICAL MANHOLES
11	12	3	14	ELECTRICAL DUCT BANK
12	13	5	14	PULL IN POWER FEEDER

FIG. 9.6 *CPM input for computer.*

I	J	DUR-ATION			DESCRIPTION	START		FINISH		TOTAL FLOAT
						EAR	LAT	EAR	LAT	
0	1	3	1	1	CLEAR SITE			3	3	0
1	2	2	1	2	SURVEY AND LAYOUT	3	3	5	5	0
2	3	2	1	1	ROUGH GRADE	5	5	7	7	0
3	4	15	1	7	DRILL WELL	7	7	22	22	0
3	6	4	1	3	WATER TANK FOUNDATIONS	7	8	11	12	1
3	9	10	1	1	EXCAVATE FOR SEWER	7	11	17	21	4
3	10	1	1	1	EXCAVATE ELECTRICAL MANHOLES	7	20	8	21	13
3	12	6	1	4	OVERHEAD POLE LINE	7	23	13	29	16
4	5	2	1	5	INSTALL WELL PUMP	22	22	24	24	0
5	8	8	1	5	UNDERGROUND WATER PIPING	24	24	32	32	0
6	7	10	1	6	ERECT WATER TOWER	11	12	21	22	1
7	8	10	1	5	TANK PIPING AND VALVES	21	22	31	32	1
8	13	2	1	5	CONNECT WATER PIPING	32	32	34	34	0
9	11	5	1	5	INSTALL SEWER AND BACKFILL	17	21	22	26	4
10	11	5	1	4	INSTALL ELECTRICAL MANHOLES	8	21	13	26	13
11	12	3	1	4	ELECTRICAL DUCT BANK	22	26	25	29	4
12	13	5	1	4	PULL IN POWER FEEDER	25	29	30	34	4

FIG. 9.7 *Computer output. (From James J. O'Brien, "CPM in Construction Management," McGraw-Hill Book Company, New York, 1965. By permission of the publishers.)*

Figure 9.6 shows the CPM input, and Fig. 9.7 the computer output for Fig. 9.2, the site-work example. In this case, the output is in the standard I-J, or index, listing. Other output listings which can be had at a nominal cost are early-start listing, critical work only, work by category, late start, and others. A caution is in order: the computer can generate thousands of pieces of paper. However, these are useful only if used. People who are expected to use the computer results must specify the computer output or sort listing which they prefer.

After the initial computation run, the computer results must be evaluated. The basic method for this is to trace the critical path on the network and to compare the end result with the desired schedule. Usually, two or more adjustment runs to the basic CPM run are required in order to achieve the required schedule. Once this has been established and reviewed, the CPM output is established as the project schedule.

Project Monitoring

After the construction CPM plan and schedule have been established, both must be evaluated and maintained on a regular basis. An unmonitored schedule rapidly becomes obsolete. Maintenance on a regular basis is not technically difficult since usually 90 to 95 percent of the original plan remains correct for the life of the project.

Frequency of updating depends upon the project, but semimonthly or monthly reviews are usually specified. In some major programs resident scheduling teams are used. For each updating, raw computer results should be summarized into a narrative report. Each updating is in effect a complete reapplication of the CPM technique. Logical sequences and estimates are revised as necessary, and a new computation is made. Where the changes are minor in nature, recomputation may be deferred. On an individual updating basis, the effort required is perhaps less than 10 percent of the initial CPM effort. However, since this is done on a regular basis, the updating procedure involves two-thirds of a complete CPM effort for a CPM-controlled project.

The cost-control advantages of CPM are most obvious during the initial project plan preparation. The communication realized during the early discussions and the effectiveness of CPM in clarifying the factors involved in a project are obvious cost-saving factors. Then after the CPM plan has been calculated, the identification of critical and near-critical activities is a second cost factor, since it permits concentration of resources on the time-consuming areas. The critical areas are not always intuitively obvious. The Corps of Engineers planning group preparing a CPM diagram for a canal installation agreed that the CPM preparation was invaluable, but that pile driving would be on the early critical path. Surprisingly, the computation showed pile driving to be noncritical because of an improved plan which enabled them to utilize two pile-driving rigs concurrently. A real-estate operation later in the project replaced pile driving on the critical path. The shift in critical path was due to better planning, but the value of the improved pile driving was almost lost because the ramifications of the plan improvement had not been recognized in all areas.

The updating of the CPM plan and use of it during the life of the project is more routine but provides the majority of the cost-control factors.

In planning a high-rise apartment building, the early portion of the plan was keyed to a three-day, form-and-pour cycle per floor. The planner accepted this input, but conditioned this inclusion upon performance in the field. Actually, the field team did even better than the office planners envisioned. A two-day per floor cycle was achieved. However, CPM monitoring flagged the not-so-obvious fact that the riser work (Fig. 9.8) had now become critical because of its slower pace. When this was recognized in a routine CPM updating, the riser work was expedited to maintain the project acceleration achieved during the concrete cycle. In this case, CPM was not responsible for the very excellent acceleration in the concrete cycle but did maintain these savings.

Time advantages realized through CPM will necessarily be relative

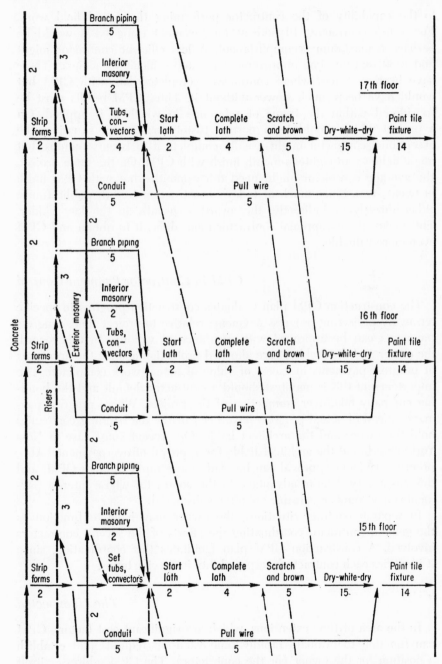

FIG. 9.8 *CPM for high rise, vertical configuration. (From James J. O'Brien, "CPM in Construction Management," McGraw-Hill Book Company, New York, 1965. By permission of the publishers.)*

to the capability of the contractor performing the actual field work. For a top contractor, 10 percent improvement using CPM would be perhaps a maximum accomplishment. A less efficient contractor might find a 30 percent time improvement not too difficult to achieve. There have been instances where contractors completed late with CPM but would have been much slower without it. Thus, CPM results must be considered within the frame of reference in which it is applied. On a project which would be a normal twenty-four-month situation, the exceptional contractor might usually complete it in twenty months, but might achieve an eighteen-month finish with CPM. On the same project, the average contractor might need thirty months, but with CPM finish in twenty-two. Since much of today's construction is with public funds, either directly or indirectly, the award is usually to the low bidder. This makes the exceptional contractor more difficult to obtain and CPM even more valuable.

CPM in Contractor Payment Control

The construction CPM plan evaluates construction progress in specific terms. By projecting progress payments relative to project time, progress payments can be approved with assurance of validity. In this regard, the owner and the architect are afforded protection against the approvals of progress payments in excess of value of actual work completed. The importance of this is manifest should a contractor default and the bonding company take over completion of the project. Where progress payments ahead of actual progress have been made, the bonding companies hold the owner and the architect liable. One recent court case in New York State found the architect liable for approval of overpayments. Also, progress-payment approval can be made more rapid through CPM, and this has a very definite advantage to the contractor whose interest payments on accounts receivable are often substantial.

In separate-contract situations, the owner may have to function as the general contractor coordinating the efforts of the several contractors involved. A construction CPM plan facilitates this coordination, since it identifies each contractor's responsibility in specific terms.

The Unexpected

In the area of time extensions, which are significant cost factors, CPM can function to evaluate rapidly time-extension requests and establish a position for the owner (or the contractor). The CPM addresses itself to specifics, a more factual position is taken, making settlement easier to effect in reducing the role of personalities in settlement. If the contractor has a legitimate claim for an extra, the CPM plan will substantiate the time aspects. CPM was used on one major project to demonstrate why the contractor should not be pressed for more than a half million dollars in liquidated damages. The contractor used the construction CPM plan to demonstrate the effects of three different unforeseen circumstances: unusually bad weather, loss of special dredging equipment by fire, and time lost doing extra work. The presentation demonstrated the effect of the three causes combined, and also could identify the effect of any one or two of the others alone. This clear CPM presentation gave the owner sufficient basis not to press for liquidated damages. This was the position which the owner preferred but as a public agency could not accept without clear proof.

Most projects face one or more major situations involving factors beyond their control. The spector of uncontrollable conditions is often raised as an objection to CPM planning. The question is asked: How can CPM account for floods, fires, strikes, labor shortages, wartime material shortages, and other unforeseen factors? Obviously, CPM is not clairvoyant, but a positive and well-defined plan can accept and evaluate these factors as they become evident. Introducing immediately any of these unforeseen factors into the network, a rapid evaluation of the actual time extension can be realized. Sometimes, application during a situation such as a protracted strike can point out work-arounds, or at least present the owner with a realistic evaluation of the overall effect of his problem.

Costs and Benefits

In terms of dollars, the benefits and cost of CPM will depend upon the project involved. In projects valued from 2 to 10 million dollars, a complete CPM application usually costs from 0.3 to 0.6 percent of the construction value. A useful outline control CPM can be prepared for even less and maintained on an adequate basis. Generally, the returns from CPM are directly proportional to the input. This input also includes the cost investment. Naturally, there is a point of diminishing returns. This is particularly felt on small contracts. CPM can be a useful concept on projects as small as custom housebuilding, but these projects cannot carry a professional CPM treatment. The answer here usually is staff CPM training. The prime benefits of CPM would include the following:

1. Minimizing time extensions by appraisal of true time effect

2. Ensuring against large lapses due to undiscovered circumstances, such as long-lead deliveries

3. Development of work-around solutions to problems, using the network as a test basis

4. Serving as time base for liquidated damages

5. Promoting coordination of the contract

6. Forming basis for scheduling owner and architect participation to avoid claims for extras for delays to contractors.

CPM during the Design Phase

The design phase offers two major opportunities for CPM application. The first of these is the planning of the design phase itself, which now approaches the actual field construction period in length. The second application is a preconstruction plan to establish a reasonable schedule.

The CPM planning of the design phase offers a great potential for time gains. It is true that the design phase is generally noncomplex for the typical building project. Many activities can occur concurrently, and the problem is more one of resource allocation of the architect-engineer staff than one of sequential planning. However, there are many reviews, and checkpoints which must be passed during the design. Particularly in public work, many of these are agency reviews. One major university project which seemed near advertisement in New York lost more than one year in the complexities of agency review. Clear identification of these areas can be of mutual benefit to the architect-engineers as well as the owner in anticipating review requirements and placing responsibility upon the owner to expedite his own decisions and reviews. The owner often feels that design work-arounds can be utilized. While this is true, the more usual practice is for the architect-engineer to employ patience, waiting until clear decisions are reached. Economically this is sound to the design agency, but in the overall picture expensive to the owner. In today's fast pace, the owner must "fish or cut bait," and a CPM plan is a tactful way to present situations to him.

The CPM plan for the design phase is usually noncomplex, generally in the range of 100 to 1,000 activities. Today, many programs, particularly on college campuses, involve several design agencies. Here, the design CPM can be very important in coordinating the efforts. Also, review by agencies involved in funding but not directly involved in the project can be devastating in their delaying effect unless properly anticipated.

Prebid Plan

The establishment of project schedules is a joint owner-architect decision based upon the owner's needs and the architect's judgment. In the past, because of the lack of a definitive method of construction forecasting, this decision has usually been arrived at rather casually.

With the development of CPM, the forecasting method has been made available. Since 1962, many CPM applications have been made prior to the award of contract. CPM studies are made to develop a reasonable construction schedule and to identify intermediate goals.

The typical construction schedule has not always been realistic, often reflecting in hopeful fashion the owner's needs whether realistic or not. The preliminary CPM plan is particularly concerned with important intermediate relationships. In an airport fuel installation the CPM construction plan showed that computer manufacture and installation for the flow-control system would be critical and that the balance of the installation could have been completed in six months less time. In this case a prebid CMP had not been done, but if it had the owner would have foreseen the situation and purchased the complex computer unit. In another pipeline project, it was assumed (without CPM) that pipe laying would be critical. In actuality, the compression stations became the controlling area. When this was recognized, the company delayed pipe laying and reinvesting many millions in construction funds for a one-year period. While it saved a substantial amount, the owner noted that early use of CPM would have saved many dollars in interest.

With the prebid CPM plan, the project is thought through in detail months sooner than is usually the case. More important, the problems are identified before the owner is committed to a contract, and solutions can be worked out and specified in the construction document. This precontractual identification of problems keeps control in the owner's hands and may avoid punitive extras.

While the primary purpose of the prebid CPM plan is the establishment of a realistic schedule and identification of important precontractual decisions, a secondary purpose is the establishment of a legal base for the enforcement of liquidated damages. The prospect of such enforcement has little attraction for either the owner or the architect. However, it is the most potent measure available to press for timely completion where normal measures fail. The prebid CPM plan is used to set a schedule by developing *one* plan for completing the project. However, this plan should not be imposed upon the contractor as *the* plan to be followed. If the contractor working on a fixed-price contract is required to follow the owner's specified implementation plan and encounters difficulties as a result, the owner could well be liable for damages as well as a time extension. However, if the prebid CPM plan demonstrates the reasonability of the construction schedule, the liquidated-damages requirement has immediate validity. Where there is no backup for the schedule, contractor often has a ready-made loophole to liquidate damages, since he will claim that the schedule was not reasonable. The AEC used CPM in its court presentation of a liquidated-damages claim against a contractor, and in the same case the contractor used CPM to support a defense. (The AEC won.)

CPM Specification

In specifying the use of CPM on a project, the path of least resistance is to require with a single phrase "the contractor shall apply CPM to the project." There are some major projects under some large agencies which use a specification not much more sophisticated than this. While this can produce positive results for contractors who have had CPM experience and are cooperative, the practice is not recommended. The concrete section in most specifications today is still several pages in length, although the phrase "3,000 lb concrete" serves, fairly well, to describe what is desired. CPM is rather intangible and difficult to specify. The experience and qualifications of the CPM planning group, whether the contractors' own or furnished by others, should be carefully specified. The actual CPM section of the specification will vary with the type of project, bidder qualifications, level of CPM application, etc. The specification should, of course, be sufficiently clear to state the CPM expectations. In general it should include:

1. The required schedule, including interim dates and occupancies
2. Procedures to be followed in preparation and approval of the CPM working plan
3. Procedure for and frequency of CPM progress evaluations
4. The extent of computer services and output format
5. Responsibilities of the contractors in meeting this schedule
6. The method of schedule enforcement

If a prebid CPM study has been made, the results can be made available to the bidders in a variety of ways:

1. Prebid plan can be incorporated in the bidding documents; however, this can imply that the plan is binding if not clearly identified as informational only.
2. Prebid CPM plan and schedule can be issued as an informational addendum.
3. Prebid CPM plan and schedule can be discussed at prebid conference.
4. Prebid plan and schedule can be made available at the architect's or owner's offices.

Capital Programming

CPM offers a great potential when used in capital programming and budgeting. Of course, at the budgeting stage, project definitions are usually very hazy. Nevertheless, broad-sketch CPM outlines can be used to establish a time base for capital programming. The Philadelphia School District's half-billion-dollar capital program was budgeted on a CPM time base. The application was simple, but effective.

At the budgetary planning stage, much more is often known about the project than is immediately obvious. In programming a Navy transmitter installation, a ten-arrow network demonstrated that the station could not become operational at the required time. This triggered an immediate work-around, and the construction was phased into an interim operation and the final configuration. The station was on line when needed. However, if the traditional design and construction cycle had been followed without this preconsideration, the project would have been about six months late. Since cost factors at this stage are very broad-based, CPM planning can have tremendous impact. As CPM experience broadens, and in-house staff gain more experience, it can be anticipated that sketch CPM will rapidly gain in significance during the capital-programming stage.

TEN

Bohdan O. Szuprowicz

Computer
Cost Analysis

During the last few years the use of computers as aids in computation or more properly as information-processing systems has grown in an unprecedented manner. It is only appropriate, therefore, that such a powerful processing device should be given serious consideration as an aid in devising, checking, and monitoring any system of cost control.

In considering computer analysis certain facts should be borne in mind by those who wish to embark on such a course of action. The computer is not an electronic brain, and it will not produce answers to questions. What can be expected is rapid and accurate processing of information submitted in strict, predetermined format. This processing takes place according to procedures developed by the user and expressed precisely in the form of statements of a computer program. It is also often not understood that once a program is developed and checked out to perform a certain accounting procedure, there is no guarantee of acceptable or even meaningful results unless the input data submitted for processing is meaningful and acceptable to begin with. However, the information available as input is often incomplete, approximate, or perhaps inaccurate within some known limits. It is in situations like these where simulation becomes a valuable method, and the computer the means by which it can be performed.

Whatever the cost-control system of any prospective computer user today, the chances are that when he decides to use computers to implement it, the cost-control system itself is unlikely to undergo any significant change. Rather, a computerized procedure, or simply a program, will be produced which will explicitly define all of the steps taken in a cost-control cycle. Attempts will be made to include foreseeable alternative courses of action and checks for possible invalid information input. This effort to formalize a cost-control system will in itself demand a searching analysis of either the existing or the conceived system as it is assembled. The system-analysis work will often uncover deficiencies or loopholes in an existing system and is often considered a valuable investigation even if no steps to computerize the system are taken.

The advantages of having a computer cost-control program developed are twofold. First is the previously mentioned capability to simulate the operation of the real-life cost-control system with little expenditure in time and money. A simulation makes possible the study of a system to find out what would happen if a certain course of action is chosen rather than another. This is clearly evidenced in the critical path method with cost features, where the effect of alternative courses of action can be studied in terms of project duration and project cost. Numerous possibilities can be studied using a CPM program and well-chosen input data and a particular course of action decided upon, depending on the objective for which an optimum is being sought. The CPM cost features is primarily a time-cost relationship (Fig. 10.1) attached to all activities which allow of alternative costs and durations.

However, the function, or product-oriented work-breakdown structure, of Program Evaluation and Review Technique (PERT) cost may prove more attractive to those who are interested in continuous project cost control. This illustrates the second advantage of a computerized cost-control system. Although the PERT cost system is in most cases a cost-accounting method rigidly attached to a project-network plan, this is not mandatory. The cost features of PERT cost can be used as a cost-control device even where no network exists. The system is really built around a function-oriented work-breakdown structure (Fig. 10.2) and is designed to periodically reestimate and compare with original budgeting the cost of work under way.

The work-breakdown structure is the framework upon which the PERT cost system operates. At the lowest level of the work-breakdown structure, the cost of work required to perform work in each particular specialty during a regular period of time is accumulated. Various summations and cost breakdowns are available both on periodic and cumulative

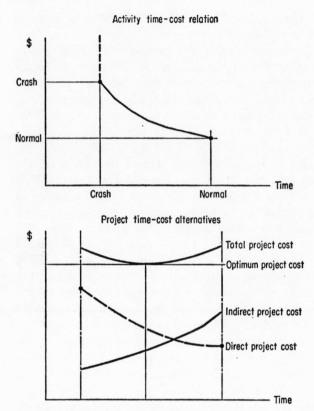

FIG. 10.1   *Time-cost relationships.*

bases once the information is collected and entered into the system.

The important point to remember is that once a certain amount of information is collected and entered into a system of computerized cost control there are many operations that can easily be performed which may yield very useful results to the user. This is so even if existing "off-the-shelf" programs do not produce results in precisely required form. Simple post-processing routines can be developed to do the work cheaply and efficiently. This is not often realized, and considerable time and money are spent in duplicating existing systems simply because the output or input is not in the acceptable or traditional format.

It would be unfair to expect the architect and the engineer to know what computers and what programs are of value to him and for what application. Increasingly, large companies appoint internal consultants or computer-application specialists, whose sole purpose is to investigate, research, and evaluate suggested areas where computer analysis can

(Cost accumulation points and levels)

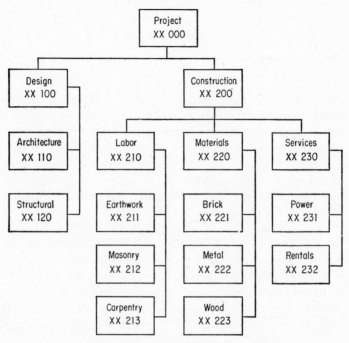

FIG. 10.2   *Work breakdown structure.*

prove of value. Smaller companies, architects, and partnerships cannot justify such expenditure, and yet if they do not keep informed about the latest, fastest, and most accurate methods of estimating and controlling their costs they risk being left out by more efficient competition.

Where to Get Services

In order to keep in step and yet not incur unnecessary costs, the small prospective user can now turn to a whole new breed of problem-solving or consulting organizations. Basically, there are five types of firms whose services may prove of value to anyone seeking to computerize his operation without actually installing a computer on his own premises. These are:

1. Service bureaus
2. Computer manufacturers' data-processing centers
3. Management consultants
4. Certified public accounting firms
5. Banks

Of the above, the independent service bureau proper, with an established clientele and reputation, is probably the best choice for architects. However, the other possibilities should also be given consideration and may in certain instances prove advantageous.

The Service Bureau

In a service bureau, the service revolves around a computer installation which is either leased from the manufacturer or wholly owned by the operating firm. Computer time is available to all comers on a twenty-four-hour basis—often seven days a week. Usually a service bureau maintains a library of ready-made programs and monitoring systems for a variety of applications. While some smaller service bureaus specialize in particular types of applications, generally the computer is available to the user for any application whatsoever.

Most service bureaus also maintain a staff of systems analysts and programmers to develop software for clients or to make modifications in existing programs to fit particular requirements. The services of these people are also available and should always be considered as additional to any computer time used. A service bureau is very advantageous to the user who has programming and systems-analysis capability of his own. He can develop his own program and use computers of one or more service bureaus as required.

If the cost of developing a program by a service bureau approaches that of hiring a good systems analyst to establish an in-house capability, it may be good business to follow the latter course. An in-house systems analyst can develop and implement a cost system and probably, by knowing his firm more intimately, do a better if not quicker job of it. Also, he can find other possible applications and become an internal consultant on all matters involving computer processing. His advice may be invaluable on such questions as whether to use a computer for a particular operation or whether it will be economical or feasible in the long run.

In using any service-bureau machines, it is also advisable to find out what backup facilities are available in case of machine malfunction or unavailability of machine time at short notice. It is usually advisable to go to a service bureau which has more than one computer of the same type or can provide access to one in an emergency. All of the above points, as well as responsibility for erroneous or incorrect processing, should be discussed and settled before any commitments are made by the computer-time user. A little research and investigation will save him considerable inconvenience—if not expense—in the long run.

Computer Manufacturers' Data-Processing Centers

To an outsider, a data-processing center may appear almost identical in operation to the service bureau. In fact, because of the computer manufacturers' brand names under which such centers are operated, they may appear more inviting than a lesser-known service bureau. However, while some of these centers will provide excellent service, their prime function is to support the sale and leasing of computer equipment and to demonstrate its capability to the prospective computer buyer. These centers are not really in competition with service bureaus and do not necessarily have to show a profit on their operation. A prospective computer user should beware of being lured by a low price or free system development, which may leave him with only a choice of either leasing or buying a computer which he did not want or need in the first place. While a solution can be found by making arrangements with someone already using such a computer, such arrangements may prove inconvenient or costly, and certainly the user will seldom have priority or backup in emergency. Therefore, unless one contemplates one's own computer installation or simply seeks education in computers, the manufacturers' data-processing center is not the most advantageous service.

Management Consultants

Most management consultants today maintain a group on their staff which can perform excellent systems analysis, programming, and implementation of cost-control systems. These groups provide services which are somewhat more expensive than service-bureau professionals for comparable work. However, on investigation, one can almost certainly find a group which has talent and whose fees are acceptable. Management consultants, whether large or small, seldom maintain a computer installation and usually make arrangements with service bureaus to obtain machine time as it is required.

There may be an advantage in retaining management consultants to do a job where considerable machine time is involved, as such groups may have standing arrangements with service bureaus and obtain cheaper computer-time rates because of extensive use of machines. Such discounts indirectly may pass to the user and would not be available to him otherwise. In dealing with consultants, however, one should always make sure whether machine-time expenditure is included in their fee or whether it is an additional expense.

Certified Public Accountants

Most large, well-known certified public accounting firms today operate management consulting groups within their organizations. The main purpose of such consulting groups is to provide services to existing clients of the certified public accountants in their normal course of business. Often, however, the management consulting services are also available to others.

Cost control and cost accounting systems, such as PERT cost or CPM, are certainly in this category. Again, as in the case of pure management consulting groups, certified public accountants may have arrangements with service bureaus or banks for computer time availability and may enjoy advantages not otherwise available to an architect. In considering computerized cost-control systems the certified public accountant may prove of considerable value, because of the nature of his business and, perhaps, because of possible prior relationships between him and the architect.

Banks

While this is the latest type of computer service bureau to come into existence, it is growing very fast and provides advantages to those who possess their own systems analysis and programming capability. Banks were one of the first large, commercial institutions to recognize the value of the computer in their operations and to install their own computers. They presently can account for a considerable number of years of systems-analysis and computer-operations experience.

In time the computerized systems of banks have improved considerably with better software and hardware, and many banks now find excess machine time available which they are willing to sell to those who need it. Primarily, this time is available to their clients, but most architectural firms maintain relations with some bank and therefore qualify directly. The computer time available through banks may be at rates considerably below those offered by service bureaus, which are probably the highest in the business. This is understandable, since the service bureau derives its income solely from selling machine time and associated programming services, while banks sell excess time which costs them practically nothing. The disadvantages here lie in restrictions on types of machines available and their availability at times which may prove inconvenient for some strictly scheduled, recurring computer operations. Also except for a few instances the systems analysis and programming services of banks are not generally available to machine-time users.

One other source of computer services is now appearing on the scene. This is the machine-time broker who acts as a middleman for banks, insurance companies, airlines, oil companies, and other enterprises which operate their own computer centers and find themselves with excess time that they are willing to sell. The broker represents such companies and offers computer time on a variety of machines and in a variety of locations. One can obtain better terms by dealing directly with such companies; however, the burden of finding out who has machine time available—and when—may not always be practical. The broker is unlikely to provide help in systems analysis and programming, and unless the user has his own capability and a good knowledge of problems involved in computer operations the use of such services is not recommended.

Cost of Services

Any organization considering the use of computers for the first time would do well to invest in a little education of its staff in general principles of computer use and operations. Before deciding whether or not a cost-control system should be computerized, it is well worth the time and expense to investigate the economic and practical feasibility of the proposition. There may often exist valid reasons to go ahead with computerization, even if not immediately economically justified, when marketing considerations or long-term effects are scrutinized. But it is probably also true that the question "do we really need computers" is not asked often enough.

Assuming, however, that a decision to use computers is made, there are various factors that will contribute to the cost of development and operation of such a system. As may be seen in the table below, the more the user undertakes to do himself, the more effective and cheaper will his operation become. Some phases of any computerized system, it is true, cannot be performed by the user, but there are many that can, and should be, since leaving such tasks to consultants may result in unnecessarily retaining highly priced personnel to perform simple functions. While this situation cannot be prevented in all instances, it certainly pays to investigate thoroughly what effort is to be undertaken by whom and at what price. The checklist following indicates functions likely to be necessary in systems design and computer operations and price ranges for use of equipment and personnel.

Function	*Dollar range of hourly rates*
Consulting, problem definition	25–45
Systems analysis, system design	17–30
Programming, coding, computer operations	10–18
Card punching, card verifying	4–6
Use of EAM equipment, sorting, reproducing, interpreting, etc.	6–10
Small computers, IBM 1401 type	50–75
Medium-size computers, GE 225, IBM 7070, CDC G-20	150–300
Large-scale computers, IBM 7094, CDC 3600, Univac	300–650

The above cost ranges are those prevailing in service-bureau operations and are probably the highest likely to be encountered by a prospective computer user. In addition to costs for functions listed, there are other expenditures which are often overlooked and which may add considerably to cost of computerization. Use of computer centers requires access to and from such centers and is time consuming. Therefore, travel costs, messenger services, hotel and motel expenditures, telephones, and purchase or use of punched cards, magnetic tapes, and specialized stationery must be considered. The implementation of certain control systems, such as CPM or PERT cost, involves further the time of personnel in planning, estimating, reviewing, and updating an operating computerized system. Taking the implementation of various CPM, PERT, and PERT cost systems as a guide, the total costs of application of such a system tends to be accounted for as in the example below.

As an example, consider the use of CPM with cost features to evaluate and control the work flow and cost accumulation in construction of an office building. Of necessity in a hypothetical case like this, certain assumptions must be made. CPM as a computerized system is chosen here as an example, because it is a simple and effective tool if properly implemented and easy for a newcomer to undertake.

The first assumption is that the work to be performed is represented by a network of about 1,000 activities. This network need not have any particular relation to project size, since small networks may represent large projects and more detailed networks may be used for smaller projects. The choice, within limits, is dictated by existing resources of the construction enterprise and the amount of control it wishes to undertake by using such computerized methods. Often such an application is a duplication of existing management and accounting controls and may not appear to save time or money if used in this manner. Assuming, however, that a task force exists to implement the system and that this team has sufficient authority to ask questions and suggest courses of action to be undertaken, one can arrive at the out-of-pocket cost of implementation as follows:

System Organization	*Cost*
Consultant 1 week (40 hr @ 30)	$1,200
Coding, computer-input preparation (1,000 cards)	500
Keypunching, keyverifying (approx. 100 cards per hr)	100
3 computer simulation runs	375
Output analysis and preparation	75
Total initial cost	$2,250

At this point, an acceptable plan of work and cost assignments exists and work may commence accordingly. Some effort must be now undertaken to monitor actual performance against the plan, but this is usually done by company personnel and does not present an out-of-pocket expenditure. The total cost of maintaining the computerized control will, however, increase with each updating of the plan and cost estimates, which may take place every month in an average operation. Each such review, assuming about 20 percent of changes and reestimates, will be priced as follows:

System Updating	*Cost*
Analysis, updating 10 hr @ $20	$ 200
Coding, computer-input preparation (200 cards)	100
Keypunching, keyverifying (200 cards)	20
2 simulation runs	250
Total periodic cost	$ 570

Therefore, if the project duration is expected to approximate one year, it is reasonable to expect about ten updating and reestimating cycles. Total cost of computerization will then become:

Initial cost	$2,250
10 periodic updates (10 × 570)	5,700
Total	$7,950

The above figure can be reduced fairly substantially if some of the operations are undertaken by internal personnel who may become available. However, any organization considering use of computer analysis for the first time should consider the costs as presented above.

It is therefore possible to project from the cost of data processing alone an approximate total cost of development and implementation of a computerized control system. The percentages presented in the example are not of course rigid in all systems work, but the pattern appears to be of that order in systems requiring continuous man-machine collaboration. With improvements in computer hardware and particularly in input and output devices and remote time-sharing access stations, data-processing costs will be less in time as service bureaus become more and more like information-processing utilities and use of computers becomes even more extensive. But such systems are more complex than those in use at present, and education gained today by a user in a batch-process operation may prove invaluable to operate economically and stay ahead tomorrow.

PART FOUR

Getting Costs
under Control
at the Beginning

ELEVEN

Rolf Sklarek, AIA

Budgeting of
Probable Costs

One of the most distinguishing characteristics of a preliminary budget is the fact that it constitutes the first written opinion on probable future costs of the building, in definite dollar amounts, which the client receives from the architect. Such first figures, whether or not they coincide with the client's preconceived ideas, have the uncanny tendency to implant themselves firmly in the client's mind. Should any misunderstandings on costs occur during later stages of a project, a critical look will always find these first budget figures at the root of the argument. No matter how much the original budget has been "qualified" and regardless of how well any subsequent revision will be documented—this first budget, prepared under most difficult circumstances, can never be fully voided as long as the project is alive.

Unlike estimates, a budget is prepared at a time when definite and detailed information on the project is not as yet available. Quantity takeoffs and accurate evaluation of special conditions are not possible at budget time, and at best, the budget analyst has at his disposal such tenuous information as a very rough description of project scope, tentative ideas on types of construction and finishes, and, if he is fortunate, a single-line sketchy layout. Very seldom,

151

indeed, will the client's map of the project site be in the form of a useful topographic survey at this time; soil conditions, water-table elevations, and information on existing or available utilities remain a matter of speculation to be resolved at a later date. In addition no definite information will yet be available on such cost-influence items as actual timing of construction, required off-site work, the bidding climate at a future date, special requirements of the client usually born and developed at a much later time, and many more items.

Estimates, produced at a later time on the basis of at least some definite information, are relatively easy to prepare when compared with preliminary budgets. The preparation of such early budgets is in effect a preliminary design activity, and all future design and detailing efforts as well as future estimates will have to live with the budget in one way or another. No effort should be spared, therefore, in budget preparation, and as in all professional services, a large amount of care, judgment, ingenuity, and foresight is required in this phase of the work. The budget must represent a realistic forecast of probable project costs based to a very large degree on carefully considered assumptions. To make a budget arbitrarily too high in order to avoid a possible future squeeze play is no solution at all. Such a procedure can quickly kill the chances of the project's realization; it must also be remembered that a budget that is too high is just as wrong and unrealistic as one that proves to be too low. Budgeting must be considered and treated as a highly sensitive creative design activity.

A Budget Is the First Step

Why then in the face of all the difficulties and possible dire consequence, it may be asked, are budgets necessary at such an early state in the project? Why not rather wait for the time when more definite information will be available, and an estimate can be prepared? Why all this rush—what is the real purpose of the preliminary budget?

The answer to these questions is really quite simple, once preliminary budgeting has been accepted as a design function—and closer inspection will disclose it as being an urgent and major one. The preliminary budgeting will be found not to be a necessary evil at all but a very useful tool for orderly and logical, yes even imaginative, design. The much maligned limitations which a budget so often dictates will many times be found actually to stimulate designers and lead them to non-routine solutions. Such a tool, such a stimulus, is of course needed early in the creative process.

The client, who needs a budget in order to evaluate the economic feasibility of the project, is entitled to a forecast of probable project cost before too much design time has been spent and certainly before any layout might become frozen. Even though some clients may think that they have thoroughly explored and evaluated the economic aspects of the contemplated improvements, later discussion in this chapter will show that this isn't necessarily so.

If properly handled and fully developed, the preliminary budget can, at the very outset, assure that architect and client are talking about the same thing, the same scope of work, the same type of investment, the same quality of building, even the same amount of professional fees.

The Budget Analyst

The budget analyst, the person preparing the budget, is charged with a huge responsibility. His judgment and his opinion expressed in the form of a budget may make or break a project. His is the task of laying the foundation upon which the work of the architectural and engineering design team will be based, and it is his budget which will remain the basis of all economic considerations until contractors bid proposals eventually either confirm or disprove it. All future estimates, based on more developed information, must, in order to be useful, be by necessity a logical refinement of the budget analyst's early work.

This is not the work for an outsider, nor for a consultant, nor for a mere technician. While contractors may be helpful in the refinement of later estimates, they cannot assist in this early stage of design, architecturally or economically. What this job needs is an architect, a designer, an imaginative, resourceful, and experienced person with long standing in the particular architect's office. He must be fully familiar, by experience, with the firm's design philosophy, with its design and detail vocabulary—and a few single lines, possibly with reference to other of the firm's projects, must give him meaningful information which no mere technician or outsider could possibly fathom. In addition to all the above, he must be thoroughly familiar with bidding and construction techniques and the business end of construction.

The budget analyst will, of course, need the cooperation of, and information from, special technicians, engineers, and designers experienced in comparative pricing of structural, mechanical, electrical, and civil engineering work. On the other hand, he must himself also be analytically minded enough to question critically all such specialized information supplied to him. And he must be completely incorruptible, even with regard to strong suggestions from his superiors or the client for a budget which, in his opinion, would be too low. A "yes-man" won't do in this job.

Architects, by tradition, have generally in the past stayed away from this kind of activity and considered it almost as menial work. Even in teamwork, many an architect wants to be identified with the more glamorous aspects of the profession—visual design—and wants to leave the chores of cost control to "others."

The true and effective budget analyst is, therefore, a rare person indeed. It is hoped, however, that more and more architects will begin to recognize construction costs and the budget as a creative stimulus. Placing more emphasis on the field of budgeting and cost control can help greatly to enhance the relationship of the profession to its clients and to the community as a whole.

The Target

To call a budget "realistic" sounds impressive—but what does it mean? Realism with regard to project cost budgets refers to the projected dollar amount as well as to the usefulness of its form of breakdown and presentation, its adaptability to further refinement, and its use as a basis for more detailed estimates. It must also serve as a basis of comparison with budgets for similar projects and must, at the same time, lend itself to segregation into separate bidding and construction contract items.

In order to function properly, it will be necessary for the budget analyst to think of himself as a bidding contractor, but he certainly does not want to turn out to be "the low bidder." Conversely he can hardly afford to be "the high bidder" without endangering the project before it ever gets into the bidding stage. The ideal target, therefore, is a budget whose construction total falls into the middle or center-third of an anticipated competitive bid range.

At times, under the pressure of economic limitation, such a target might have to be lowered, and aim may have to be taken at a point within the lower-third of such a bid range. This is a tricky assignment, requiring a large amount of experience. But it can be accomplished within reasonable limits of accuracy. A somewhat more difficult to handle variation presents itself when bids will not be obtained by competition but rather on a negotiated guaranteed-maximum basis.

Such a target should, of course, be stated in a preamble to the budget presentation, and such statement may take a form similar to:

> The budget herein presented is not intended to reflect the lowest bid possible to be obtained. It aims at a reasonable and realistic figure which, under competitive bidding procedures, should fall somewhere within the middle-third of the range of competitive bids from high to low. While, of course, it is hoped that this will result in a certain amount of con-

tingency within the budget figure, it cannot be emphasized enough that the budget should not be reduced in the light of the above. The figures are not so much an approximation of expected actual cost, but rather expressions of recommendations for a realistic budget at this time.

The probable future bid range as well as a future negotiated dollar amount depends on many factors, some of them predictable and others completely inaccessible even to guesswork at the time of preliminary budgeting. Budget qualifications with regard to the second category will be discussed later in this chapter.

Predictable influences on the range of competitive bids from high to low can, generally, be traced to the type of bids requested, the documents issued, and the bidding procedure selected. Therefore, to a large degree, such influences are dependent on the quality and type of service rendered by the architect's team. The client is, of course, part of this team, and very often it is the client who, "looking for a miracle," makes demands in the preparation of bid documents which may result not in a miracle but actually in erratic, if not even higher than normal, bids by contractors.

The normal range of bid proposals of approximately 5 to 6 percent may widen considerably, may in fact even double, because of choices of bid documents, bid methods, bid proposal forms, type of bidders invited, and the number of bidders on the list. Generally speaking the bid range will tighten with a small number of bidders of the same "speed" invited to bid on clearly drawn proposal forms relating to clear and concise drawings and specifications.

Suffice it to state once again that the budget analyst must be thoroughly conversant with the standards of performance of his office in such matters in order to properly foresee and evaluate the range of bids to be expected under various bidding conditions. Only then will he be able to contribute creatively to the work of the total design team by correctly setting the goal and then, in turn, hitting the target.

Budget Breakdown

The target figures, once arrived at, must be broken down and organized in their presentation in such a manner to allow them to be allocated toward various categories in case of segregated bidding. Such segregation must follow a pattern which will also form a useful format to be followed in later cost control using estimates and their unavoidable revisions. The use of a standardized form for budget presentation will also make it easier to compare the anticipated cost of the project under consideration with figures obtained from previous and similar jobs.

Nothing, incidentally, will confuse and antagonize a client more than an ever-changing format in the presentation of cost information. The figures, of course, may change, but it must be easy to relate new and revised figures to earlier ones. The categories of the breakdown, therefore, should be chosen in such a way that future cost refinements can be made by further breakdown as required without a change in the basic breakdown headings.

If, for instance, based on an anticipated construction time schedule, the budget included a category "add for winter work" and an allowance of, say, 3 percent was added to cover with extra cost, it might happen that later rescheduling of the project will make winter work unnecessary. Rather than completely dropping such category, it makes more sense, in terms of cost control, to continue to show the same item with the same heading, with a notation indicating: "Per new construction time schedule of (date) not required" and showing a dollar amount of "none." The client usually understands such orderly procedures better, and the cost control history of a project will be well documented for the benefit of owner and architect alike. No surprises will come up months later when schedules change again, and open-framing work will again be required during the winter months.

Similarly, a budget category of "interior finish" may be broken down further, in estimates to follow, into actual improvement descriptions, such as partitions, doors, flooring, ceilings, millwork, and later on might still be further refined into actual trade sections, such as lathing, plastering, furring or marble, hardware, painting. The total of all such individual items should, however, still be shown under the heading of "interior finish."

Scope of the Budget

Up to this point the expression "project cost" has been used—with intent—rather than "construction cost." The budget, in order to serve all of its purposes, must include in its scope all costs to be incurred, and foreseeable as such, and the actual construction costs are only part of the total costs.

Other items to be included in the budget are not only those that only the owner can evaluate in dollar amounts (land, legal and taxes, administrative and advertising costs, etc.), but also such more definite items as architectural fees and reimbursables or off-site work which eventually will be required to make the improvements on the site perform properly. The latter may include such items as future street alignment, future sewer facilities, or even items to be done off-site during the project construction period, including additional water mains for sources of uninterrupted fire protection, bringing in additional power for x-ray or projection purposes, and signalization of adjoining road intersections. Later on in this chapter many such nonconstruction budget items will be touched upon.

Even experienced and enlightened clients too often lump together all project costs, divide by the square footage provided by the facility, and then claim that the architect planned a project with an extremely high cost per square foot. At such time, these clients may not admit, or even realize, that a good proportion of the cost is actually composed of expenditures that could be rightfully charged to land costs or that were incurred to facilitate future expansions or enlargement of the project and would be chargeable to a category possibly entitled "advance toward future expansion." Into such a category should go extra costs in foundations or columns, floor slab in lieu of lighter roof slab to support future floors, as well as larger mechanical and electrical spaces to accommodate equipment which will be installed at some future time.

A little reflection on the subject will make it clear that restricting the budget scope to actual project construction cost is no solution to the dilemma at all and will often, as in the case of provisions for future expansion, not even be possible. The best budget policy is to call out all items and to arrange them in a way that will show them clearly, either as within the scope of the architect-client agreement or as additional items.

There is a trend among developers of large projects to provide utilities to the tenants from a landlord-owned and -operated central plant, charging the tenant for such at a profit.

When this happens, the landlord, in effect, is going into the utility business in addition to real-estate ventures, and the cost of central plant, space, and equipment should be charged to such additional revenue-producing enterprise under the category often called "self-liquidating items." Examples of such items are all facilities which produce income in addition to rental income; these should include vending-machine spaces and space for other coin-operated devices, such as storage lockers, cafeterias, and even including public pay-toilet facilities. While the sum total of such items may not be significant in smaller projects, it will make a sizable difference in large improvements, such as regional shopping centers or other large institutions for lease or public use.

The budget analyst, who must eventually state his budgets in terms of dollars per sq ft of buildings, must be a penny pincher to a large degree. A two-cent difference in sq-ft cost in a home, a small office, or medical building, may not be of any consequence, but in projects involving a million or more sq ft, the impact of a total of such differences, if correctly accounted for, may sometimes spell the difference between life or death of a project.

Attention to these matters will not only be helpful to the architect in presenting his budgets but often open the eyes of even the most experienced client and developer toward a more realistic appraisal of the economics of the project.

While it is, of course, not possible within the framework of this book to give a definite prescription for each budget category, nor dollar amounts related to each, the following discussion may be helpful as a checklist in budget preparation. And reference to the sample budget form (Fig. 11.1) will be helpful in evaluation. There are, of course, many ways to set up such a form, and the format shown may be revised to suit the project. The intent here is to show the thought and the logic upon which the form should be based.

The dollar amount ranges indicated for the various categories are included here only for illustration. They represent the range of cost experience in different types of projects and are expressed in terms of dollars per square foot of rentable area. This concept of rentable area will be touched upon in a later paragraph in this chapter. These cost illustrations should not be used for actual budget preparations, and the budget analyst must use good judgment, based on experience, in order to determine actual anticipated project costs in terms of dollars per square foot.

Categories where no cost illustrations are given must be treated almost as estimates, and their evaluation will have to be based on actual calculations. It is obvious that categories such as unusual site conditions or soil conditions cannot be budgeted for unless some actual information regarding the project site is available. Should such information not be available, the category as such may be retained in the budget form, and an indication should be made that such categories have as yet not been evaluated. Such a procedure generally works out better than leaving a space blank. A notation, such as "no info. yet," will at least indicate to the client reading the budget that some figure will have to be inserted in this category at a later time. Other categories, such as landscaping or art and sign program, can be established at budget time in consultation with the owner. Since it is his project, he must participate in setting up such programs and the dollar amounts related to them.

Basic Construction Cost

This category includes all items required for the construction of the facilities, excluding all unusual conditions, as listed under other headings, but generally in accordance with published codes and standard requirements of governmental authorities and utility companies. In-

Preliminary Project Budget		Job No.		Date:
Job:		Rev. No.		Date:
Location:		Prepared by:		
Gross area:		Rental area:		Efficiency ____ %

Item	$ per sq. ft. Gross	$ per sq. ft. Rental	Total $	
1. Site work				
2. Structural frame				
3. Exterior finish				
4. Interior finish				
5. Mechanical vert. transportation				
6. Electrical work				
7. Heating, ventilating, air-conditioning				
8. Plumbing				
9. Fire protection				
Basic Building Costs			$	
10. Unusual site conditions		$		
11. Unusual soil conditions		$		
12. Off-site work		$		
13. Provisions for future expansion		$		
14. Special equipment		$		
15. Construction-time schedule		$		
16. Type of bidding and contract		$		
Unusual Building Costs			$	
17. Landscaping		$		
18. Art and sign program		$		
19. Tenant allowances (standard)		$		
20. Self-liquidation items		$		
Additional Budget Items			$	
		Sub-total	$	
21. Professional fees	$			
22. Surveys and insurance costs	$			
23. Land cost	$			
24. Legal and accounting costs	$			
25. Leasing and advertising costs	$			
26. Financing costs and taxes	$			
27. Promotion	$			
28. Pre-opening expenses	$			
29. Owner's administration costs	$			
30. Concessions to major tenants (above standard)	$			
Owner's Budget Items			$	
Total Project Budget			$	

FIG. 11.1 *Preliminary budget form.*

cluded are items 1 through 9, discussed below, and as listed in Fig. 11.1 (the sample budget form).

1. *Site Work*   This includes normal amount of grading, building excavation and backfill, paving, striping, curbs, driveways, lighting and landscape irrigation, site portion of storm drainage, sanitary drainage, electrical supply, water supply (domestic and fire loop), gas, telephone. Such work may run anywhere from 50 cents per sq ft in a small project to $2 per sq ft in a large project with a large parking area.

2. *Structural Frame*   This refers to foundations (or in the case of unusual foundation conditions such as piling, an equivalent amount, possibly represented by pile caps and grade beams), columns, girders, beams and joists, bearing walls, slabs on grade and suspended, framing of shafts, stairs, penthouses and roofs, and fireproofing of structural members where required. Structural frame costs may vary from $3 per sq ft for a one-story Type V building to $4.50 per sq ft in a high-rise building of Type I construction.

3. *Exterior Finish*   Included in this category are exterior walls (with exterior but without interior finish), free-standing walls (wing walls, etc.), entrance units, windows, store fronts, copings, flashings, caulking, roofing and waterproofing, exterior stairs and ramps, etc. Exterior finish costs may range from $1.25 per sq ft for a simple building up to $3.70 per sq ft for high-rise buildings with costly finish, such as precast concrete units hung onto a structural steel frame.

4. *Interior Finish*   This includes interior finish of exterior walls, interior partitions, doors, finish ceilings, finish flooring and bases, cabinet and millwork, painting and special wall coverings, etc. Not included in this category, however, should be interior finish work called out later under "tenant allowances." The cost of such interior finish work may range from $1 per sq ft for commercial stores, to $2.50 per sq ft for office buildings, to $3.50 per sq ft in medical buildings.

5. *Mechanical-Vertical Transportation*   This refers mainly to elevators and escalators. This category should not include such items as dumb waiters, lifts, or conveyors for the exclusive use by certain tenants.

6. *Electrical Work*   All electrical work from 5 ft outside the building, including switch gear, transformers where required, light fixtures, service to elevators, escalators, mechanical installations and signs, and all other standard outlets are in this category. Not included would be special wiring for processing purposes, x-ray, computers, or similar specialized equipment which will be listed in a separate category. The cost of such basic electrical work will run, depending upon the project's size and type, from $1.25 to $2.25 per sq ft.

7. *Heating, Ventilation, Air Conditioning*   This category, while self-explanatory, is a difficult one to budget. A number of basic concepts

must first be established before budgeting will be possible. Required decisions relate to such questions as: Heating only or air conditioning? Central plant or dispersed units? Central plant supplying heat-exchange media, hot and cold water for example, with fan coils in various locations? Climatic considerations with regard to project locations are, of course, to be taken into account at budgeting time, and it is imperative that the system forming the basis of this budget category be defined. While the HVAC concept can always be changed at a later time, the budget figure should be tied to a particular type of installation.

In projects where the developer operates a central plant at a profit by selling conditioning to the tenants, the cost of a central plant, including the cost of the space housing it, should be segregated and listed under "self-liquidating utilities" as explained earlier in this chapter. Air-conditioning costs range from $1.50 to $2.50 per sq ft depending on the type of system and the size of the project as well as on location, climate, and occupancy.

8. *Plumbing Work* This includes all interior plumbing work, sanitary and storm drainage from 5 ft outside the building line, complete with fixtures and trim, but excluding special plumbing work in excess of code or standard requirements, to be installed for the benefit of special tenants. Cost of the plumbing category may range from 60 cents per sq ft to $1 per sq ft.

9. *Fire Protection* This category basically refers to sprinkler systems, (but not fire loop already under "site work") from a point 5 ft outside the building line, or relates to fire warning systems, smoke detection systems, etc. The budget should clearly state which areas are so fire protected. Sprinkler work will range in cost from 35 cents per sq ft of protected area to 45 cents per sq ft of protected area when double sprinkling may be required. The cost of fire protection per square foot of rental area will, of course, depend upon the extent to which the various areas of the project are equipped with sprinkler system or other fire protection devices.

The second category of costs discussed here as items 10 through 16, and listed in the same way on the sample form, refers to unusual building costs.

10. *Unusual Site Conditions* This category refers to such items which make the difference between a normal, unencumbered, freely accessible site of reasonably flat grade and a site which requires demolition or special preservation of existing structures, special access roads to be built, rerouting or bridging over natural site features, such as a river or creek beds, or an abnormal amount of grading, particularly when cut and fill cannot be balanced.

11. *Unusual Soil Conditions* This includes such conditions as soil

unsuitable for normal load bearing, high water table requiring pumping, coffer-dams or excessive waterproofing, rock conditions requiring blasting, and any other ground conditions which make the construction of standard foundations and basements impossible without additional and unusual construction and costs.

12. *Off-site Work* This item relates primarily to improvements to be done outside of the actual project limits and generally involves widening or realignment of streets and highways, signalization of intersections in order to protect project access, etc. This matter has been discussed in preceding paragraphs. Many times the financial cooperation of townships can be obtained in the preparation of a budget figure for many off-site items. The estimated amount of municipal participation should be deducted.

13. *Provisions for Future Expansion* This item also has been touched upon earlier in this chapter and involves mainly the oversizing of structural members as well as electrical and mechanical facilities to serve future extension or expansion of the project. Such expansion may either take place vertically or horizontally, and appropriate allowances should be budgeted in order to facilitate such future work. The cost for such provisions are budgeted under the "unusual" category, since they are actually advanced expenditures for the different and future project and should not be included in any sums which will be used to determine the cost of the project under consideration.

14. *Special Equipment* The scope and meaning of this category should be self-explanatory. It includes all special equipment—electrical, mechanical, plumbing, or any other type—required for the business or processing operations of the occupants of the building in order to carry on their business activities. Such items include, among others, kitchen equipment, incinerators, dock levelers, trash or package chutes, conveyors, paint spray booths, pneumatic systems, and ADT provisions. In addition to the above, other equipment items should be included if they do not normally appear in projects of this kind in the locality, such as flagpoles, window-washing equipment, and communication antennas.

15. *Time Schedule* If the time schedule required by the client is shorter than the budget analyst believes feasible under normal working conditions or if the timing of construction involves critical concreting to be done during severe winter weather, then allowances should be included under this category to allow for estimated overtime required or for special winter construction procedures in order to protect the work.

16. *Type of Bid and Contract* Allowances should be included under this category, varying anywhere from 3 to 6 percent of the budgeted

construction costs, when in the opinion of the budget analyst the type of bidding required or the time allowed for bidding or the type of documents issued would induce the bidders to include "scare money" in their proposals. When contracts are let on a negotiated basis, the author as a matter of routine adds 3 percent to the budgeted construction cost.

The next categories of costs, here and on the form, are additional budgets, not actually part of the *building* construction.

17. *Landscaping* The scope of this category should include, in addition to plants, planting, and soil additives, such items as movable planters and indoor planting, benches, and certain other improvements such as outdoor fountains.

18. *Art and Sign Program* Exterior signs, project identification signs on the site, and traffic signs required in parking lots fall into this category. In addition, allowances for artwork should be made, including murals, statuary, and other items which may be commissioned from independent artists.

19. *Tenant Allowances* Since at the time of preliminary budgeting, leasing negotiations have generally not taken place as yet and tenant requirements will not be known, allowances should be made for the work which the landlord will have to perform for such tenants. Such allowances should be maximum allowances, and the leasing agent of the owner should be encouraged to obtain leases at lesser amounts for the work than the allowances multiplied by the leased area would indicate.

This category should further include an allowance for special work which the landlord may elect to furnish at his cost to certain prestige and anchor tenants. Such allowances, of course, are subject to large variations and have in the author's experience ranged all the way from $2.75 to $4.50 per sq ft of rental area. Such allowances are generally intended to cover such items as stair fronts, finish, ceilings, and interior distribution of the electrical and air-conditioning systems.

20. *Self-liquidating Utilities* This category has been discussed in previous paragraphs and need not be amplified further.

The categories of architectural and engineering fees as well as the items under "owner's budget items" (numbers 21 through 30 on the form) are self-explanatory, it is believed, and are intended to add such amounts as required to develop an overall budget for the project. Since the owner will be familiar with his contractural obligations under his agreement with the architect and since he is the one to make decisions affecting items 22 through 30, these items should be left blank by the budget analyst whose work will stop at the subtotal including the "additional budget items."

Note of Caution and of Explanation

In breaking down the total preliminary budget into the above-indicated categories, sufficient contingency should be included in each category to counteract the fact that the budget has been prepared on the basis of a minimum of definite information. This is preferable to the system of calling out a certain percentage factor as contingency, since it will not as easily lead to a bargaining session with the budget analyst and attempts to have him reduce such contingencies.

Budget Exclusions

Some budget analysts prefer not to list categories 21 through 30 within the budget and prefer to list them as exclusions from the budget. This, for certain types of clients, makes for a better and more understandable budget presentation. One system is as good as the other as long as the items required for a total project budget are either listed or specifically excluded in writing.

Budget Qualifications

A large number of assumptions have to be made in the preparation of budget figures and such assumptions should be explained in writing in order to give meaning to the projected dollar amounts. Therefore, it is necessary to make some sort of outline specification and a listing of assumptions a part of the budget presentation. This will properly define the scope of the budget in writing and will facilitate making changes at a later time when more or different information becomes available. In the interest of forestalling any possible future disputes with regard to the original preliminary budget, such a listing of assumptions should be quite extensive and specific.

Also, somewhere in the preamble to the budget presentation reference should be made to both the fact that the budget is intended to cover only such items as are called out in the outline specification and that the budget is based on the assumptions listed. A small amount of care and caution at this stage of the game by properly defining the scope of the budget and qualifying its validity can insure against an untold number of arguments at a later date.

What Is a Square Foot?

It is a customary procedure to express budget costs in terms of square foot costs. This will allow comparison, if thoughtfully done, with costs of similar projects and will allow, in many instances, adjustment of budgets by prorating when project areas are adjusted during later design stages.

The quoting of costs in terms of building area has unfortunately become a widely accepted practice without a proper definition of what is meant by it. Even though standard documents exist, defining the measurements of buildings, the gross area of a project alone does not impart too much meaning to such cost figures without reference to the actual usable area provided within its total. Confusion reigns in square-foot cost quotations, and all too often such confusion leads to interpretations of budgets which can only result in arguments and strained relations between architect and client.

A much clearer definition of costs can be obtained by quoting them in terms of number of beds in a hospital, number of seats in a theater or restaurant, number of students provided for in a school, etc. The number of such units provided in a project determines the income potential or the efficiency of the contemplated improvement, and in the last analysis, this is the prime reason for the whole undertaking. Expression of costs in terms of such units provides much better information and comparison than pure square-foot figures.

In projects primarily planned for leasing to tenants or for the owner's own use, a different unit based on areas has been developed. Since it is the usable area for the owner's own purposes, or the area which he can lease to tenants, which determines the income to be obtained from the project, costs should be based on "net rental area." The cost of the building is then brought into meaningful relationship to the revenue-producing potential of the project.

Net rental area is obtained by deducting from the gross building area all areas on which tenants will not pay rent or which are not directly contributing to the owner's own space requirements.

Such non-revenue-producing areas generally consist of public accommodations, lobbies, corridors, code-required toilets, stairs, etc., as well as functional mechanical spaces, such as shafts for elevators, mechanical risers, or other mechanical equipment spaces.

Columns and pilasters within the remaining rental area are traditionally not deducted, and the rental areas are computed to center lines of interior partitions and walls and to the glass line or equivalent distances, in the case of exterior building walls.

Expressions of cost in terms of such square footage reduced to net rental areas are, of course, higher than costs per square foot of gross building area. It is quite important that the client be made aware of the definition of the square foot so that his projections of costs will be in line with the architect's budget for the project. Since the time-honored square-foot cost, based on gross areas, is so deeply ingrained in the minds of the public, it is advantageous to call attention to these matters by relating the budget to both types of square-foot cost.

The concept of useful area, or net rental area, in addition, gives the architect and client a useful tool for comparing various schemes for a project with regard to "efficiency." Of course, efficiency is not the only factor in planning and design, but it does have to be considered.

Tools Available

Previous experience from similar projects must be the budget analyst's main tool in arriving at the unit to be used. In addition, published cost information and indices are available; when used with caution and understanding, these will be helpful in budget preparation.

Common Pitfalls

Insufficient description of the scope of work covered by the budget is probably the most prevalent source of misunderstanding. In order to avoid such misunderstandings, a preamble to the budget should explain its target, and a brief but concise outline specification and a listing of assumptions made should be part of the presentation. Figures alone, without an explanation, are meaningless and dangerous.

Another source of potential budget trouble lies in special deals which owners sometimes propose. A case in point would be owner-furnished light fixtures to be installed by the contractor. Large owners often exercise their buying power in this way with the aim of not having to pay the contractor's markup. What is often forgotten is that the advantage of such deals is nullified by the subcontractors adding into their costs the profit or rebates which they would have obtained had such purchases been made through them. Great care must therefore be exercised before lowering a budget cost for such special deals.

Contingencies are important even at such an early stage as the preliminary budget period. As outlined earlier, such contingencies should be distributed throughout the budget categories rather than showing them in a single lump sum, which may become subject to negotiation with the budget analyst—or with the client. When cuts are to be made in a budget, the client's first impulse is to be optimistic and to cut out or reduce the contingency. This should never be permitted.

Budgets, once prepared, should not be forgotten. They will have to live and stand up for a long time and must be constantly kept up to date, in writing, whenever changes occur in the scope of the work, or when further development warrants a change in the underlying assumptions. Changes should not be left to accumulate, and budget revisions should be presented to the owner, in writing, as soon as they become necessary.

It is not possible to place too much emphasis on the need for orderly and organized procedures in budget preparation. A carelessly prepared budget is nothing but insurance for future trouble. Just as visual design must be treated with sensitivity, engineering design must be based on knowledge applied with judgment and sensitivity to the creative activity of preparing a budget.

TWELVE

J. T. Greenberg

Control during Schematic Design

Creative cost control is one of the most valuable tools available to the architect in rendering a thorough, comprehensive service to his client. By maintaining careful cost control throughout the development of a project, the architect is able to assure himself and his client that the project can be built within the limits of the budget. Moreover, and of equal importance to both the client and the architect, constant review of costs enables the architect to effect truly creative design with the knowledge that every one of the client's dollars will be used to achieve the best possible result.

The feasibility of a project must be determined during its early stages. Through the use of realistic cost approximations, the architect can advise his client whether or not his requirements for the building and his proposed budget are compatible. At one extreme, he may be able to demonstrate to his client that by increasing the breadth and scope of the project and increasing his budget, a more favorable return on his investment will result. At the other extreme, the architect may find that he must recommend the abandonment of the project as economically unfeasible.

Also, during the early phases, the application of cost control makes it possible to establish a framework within which all the design disciplines can—and will—work. The first cost approximation during the programming or preschematic phase will indicate the possibilities of materials, methods, and systems to the designers. The possibilities become probabilities during schematic design, with its attendant further study of costs. If careful cost control has been applied from the first phase of the project, the probabilities can become realities within the client's budget.

A major responsibility of an architect is to design a building which meets the client's functional requirements within the budget. To meet that responsibility, the architect must use creative cost control in every phase of a project—from concept through completion of construction. At every stage of a project, cost control is very elusive. It is not a science with exact formulas subject to mathematical analysis but an art which requires imagination, knowledge of methods of construction, the development of continuous data on the use and cost of material, and visualization of the project as a whole.

There can be no such thing as cost control in a single phase of a project. To be effective, there must be an estimate or cost approximation in each phase. Cost control must be maintained and the client kept advised throughout the process. In our office, the following phases in the development of all projects are normal office procedure:

1. Programming
2. Master planning
3. Schematics
4. Preliminaries
5. Working drawings and specifications
6. Construction supervision

Cost control is mandatory throughout the development process and is effected in the following phases prior to bidding:

1. Cost approximation at preschematic
2. Cost approximation at schematic
3. Estimate at preliminary
4. Estimate at approximately one-third of completion of working drawings
5. Review of estimate one month ahead of issuing for bids

During the preschematic state, we normally develop a program which involves and incorporates the following:

1. Owner's basic philosophy on the project
2. Spaces required and their relationship

3. Identification of areas
4. Total area required
5. Total overall budget

There should also be a list of items not in the contract, such as furniture, special equipment, and Venetian blinds. There should be a list of items that are not in the contract *but* should be in the contract, such as truck scales and railroad track. The client should be forewarned of this list.

By beginning cost control in the preschematic stage, we give the designers the possibilities and the total cost figure with which they may work. When we say designers, we include architectural, structural, mechanical, electrical, elevator, and possibly other designers.

The breakdown of the cost estimate in the preschematic phase indicates that the designers have:

1. X dollars for architectural and structural trades
2. Y dollars for the mechanical trades
3. Z dollars for electrical trades
4. ZZ dollars for the vertical transportation
5. Allowance for site work

With this information (items 1 through 5) the client and the designers in all disciplines can determine the degree of refinement which may be expected of the various trades. Also, the designers will be able to approach the schematic stage with the philosophy, the functional relationships, floor areas, and detailed costs required, and, therefore, can develop a realistic solution that will reflect the needs of the client. It is important to achieve this early in the operation.

As an example, in our office, the top men in all design disciplines were involved in preschematic programming of a Federal office building. As a result, we knew in advance at the architect-engineer contract negotiation what we were expected to accomplish and what the design possibilities were under the rigid budget limitations. When we got to the finalization required at the schematic (or "tentative," as it is designated by the GSA) phase, we already had requirements and as a result had more of the answers. When we got through the schematics and submitted the estimate we found it was very close to that which we had prepared during the preschematic phase. This, then, is an indication that it is most desirable to prepare a preschematic cost appraisal on every project to avoid allowing the project to get out of focus, as so often happens.

If we follow this procedure in the preschematic phase when there are only four or five people involved, we avoid the troubles which can develop as more and more technical people get into the development of the project. This helps to avoid backtracking and going over the project to make necessary adjustments. If it can be done right the first time, we have saved ourselves and our clients much trouble and many headaches.

Schematic design in our office consists of preparing a written outline of the owner's needs; establishing the conceptual design, which defines the general arrangement and space usage of the building (including required mechanical, electrical, and other utility spaces), building masses, choice of major materials, and establishment of broad engineering requirements; and preparing a construction cost approximation. In this phase, we have determined the probabilities. To establish the above, drawings and outline specifications are required. The cost approximation must be based on, and be consistent with, the drawings and outline specifications.

In order to adhere to a cost approximation meeting the requirements of thumbnail sketches and elementary outline specifications, the following procedures are carried out:

1. The project director, all department heads, production coordinator, and manager of construction cost thoroughly review all documents available at the time and indicate their concurrence by initialing the record copy of the cost approximation and the record set of drawings which are the basis of the cost approximation.

2. It is the responsibility of the project director to see that the record is made, filed for reference, and used as the project proceeds through advancing stages.

3. Estimates given to clients should be reviewed if there is a very long lapse of time between submission and receipt of approval to proceed into the following stage. Clients should be advised that a reasonable amount of premium time is included in the estimate but that there is no allowance for unreasonable, unusual, or excessive amounts of overtime due to record construction activity or shortages of skilled labor.

There can be no provision for excessive premium time because there is no gauge by which to judge this item. However, an approximate analysis, assuming that labor is 55 to 65 percent of the total cost of a project, and assuming a normal workweek of forty hours, indicates the following:

A fifty-hour workweek has the effect of adding 12 to 15 percent to the estimate.

A fifty-five-hour workweek has the effect of adding 16 to 19 percent to the estimate.

A sixty-hour workweek has the effect of adding 20 to 25 percent to the estimate.

If the basic workweek becomes thirty-five hours, an additional 8 to 10 percent will have to be added to each of the above increases.

We require a preschematic consideration by the client on all projects before beginning the schematics. This means that we must have a program and ground rules from the client. From the program, we must be able to ascertain the following:

1. Size of the structure.

2. Approximate location and conditions of the site.

3. Is it an entirely new project?

4. Is it a revision of existing project plus the addition of a new project?

5. Use of the structure.

6. Population to be served.

7. Site utilities available.

8. Existing structures and facilities (removals required).

9. Provision for future expansion (vertical and horizontal).

10. Client limitations on construction cost.

11. Area of land available to determine the height of the structure—low rise or high rise?

Cost Approximation for the Preschematic Stage

An educated guess at the cost per square foot of a building can be made based on records of previous experience for a similar type of project. If there are no records available, the cost per square foot must be determined by preparing a rough breakdown of cost for the work of all trades.

The following is a rough guide of cost per square foot for various types of structures:

Elementary schools	$13–$16
High schools	$16–$23
Laboratories	$30–$48
Hospitals	$33–$48
Small office buildings	$18–$22
Office buildings (high-rise)	$25–$35
Office buildings (prestige)	$35–$50
Parking decks (above ground or not more than two levels below ground)	$1,500–$2,300 per car
Parking decks (four levels below ground plus several levels above ground)	$2,800–$4,500 per car

The following examples illustrate the procedure to follow if there are no records for the type project under consideration, relating all costs to the gross floor area, as determined in accordance with the AIA standard method of figuring floor areas.

Example No. 1

Assume a one-story building, 100 × 100 ft, floor area 10,000 sq ft plus a penthouse of 400 sq ft for a total area of 10,400 sq ft. The wall periphery of 400 × 12-ft story height equals 4,800 sq ft of wall surface area. Add approximately 10 percent for parapet and/or required grade beam. Use a total of 5,200 sq ft. To arrive at the building-work cost per square foot of floor area, determine the following, all in dollars per square foot:

		$/Sq ft
1.	Roof and roofing	$ 2.00
2.	Exterior wall $\dfrac{5,200 \text{ sq ft}}{10,400 \text{ sq ft} \times \$6 \text{ per sq ft}}$	3.00
3.	Slab on ground (inclusive 6 in. gravel fill)	0.80
4.	Partitions, assumed	2.50
5.	Doors	0.25
6.	Floor finishes	0.50
7.	Suspended ceilings	0.90
8.	Miscellaneous, excavation, fill, miscellaneous metal	1.55
9.	Footings and grade beams	0.50
10.	Building work	$12.00
	General conditions and contingency	2.00
	Total building work	$14.00
	Mechanical work	4.50
	Electrical work	2.50
	Total cost	$21.00

Total cost of structure = 10,400 sq ft × $21 per sq ft = $218,400

The following example illustrates the increase in per-square-foot cost in a multistory building of approximately the same floor area as the previous example.

Example No. 2

Assume a three-story building with the dimensions of 50 × 70 ft, floor area of 3,500 sq ft. Three floors of 3,500 sq ft each equals 10,500 sq ft. Exterior wall perimeter consists of 2 × 70 ft plus 2 × 50 ft for a total of 240 ft. Total wall area equals 240 × 12 ft per story × 3 stories for a total of 8,640 sq ft.

There are clients who think in terms of the cost per square foot of a building previously built—one which may not be of the same type or scope. These clients may have had experience with buildings but do not have the background for evaluating all the elements in a particular structure.

$/sq ft

1. Roof and roofing: $\dfrac{3,500 \times \$2 \text{ per sq ft}}{10,500}$ $0.70

2. Exterior wall: $\dfrac{8,640 \times \$6 \text{ per sq ft}}{10,500}$ 5.30

3. Slab on ground: $\dfrac{3,500 \times \$.80 \text{ per sq ft}}{10,500}$ 0.30

4. Supporting slabs: $\dfrac{2 \times 3,500 \times 3.50}{10,500}$ 2.50

5. Partitions   2.50
6. Doors   0.25
7. Floor finishes   0.50
8. Suspended ceilings   0.90
9. Miscellaneous   2.00
10. Footings and grade beams   0.50

11. Building work $15.45
    General conditions   2.55

    Total building work $18.00
    Mechanical work   6.00
    Electrical work   2.50
    Elevator   1.50

      Total cost $28.00

Total cost of structure — 10,500 sq ft $\times$ \$28 per sq ft = \$294,000

The following example illustrates that a very small building may have a very high cost per square foot.

Example No. 3

Assume a project of 600 sq ft floor area (20×30 ft) for which a 5-ft roof overhang is required (roof 30×40 ft), roof area 1,200 sq ft, story height 12 ft. Therefore we have the following situation:

$/sq ft

1. Wall panel: 100×12 ft $= \dfrac{1,200 \text{ sq ft} \times \$5 \text{ per sq ft}}{600 \text{ sq ft}}$ $10.00

2. Roof (assume \$2.50 per sq ft): $\dfrac{1,200 \text{ sq ft} \times \$2.50 \text{ per sq ft}}{600}$ 5.00

3. Grade beam: $100 \times 5 = \dfrac{500}{600}$ sq ft $\times$ \$3 per sq ft   2.50

4. Partitions: 70 lin. ft (movable) $\times$ \$35   4.00

5. Finishes, ceilings, doors, toilet partitions: $\dfrac{\$5,400}{600}$ 9.00

6. Mechanical work: A/C, plumbing, etc. $\dfrac{\$3,000}{600}$ 5.00

7. Electrical work: $\dfrac{\$2,100}{600}$ 3.50

    Total cost $39.00

Total cost of structure: 600 sq ft $\times$ \$39 per sq ft = \$23,400

To sum up—we establish a unit cost per square foot, either from records and past experience or from the rough approximation which we have made of all of the trades, and multiply it by the total area of the structure to derive the total budget as completely as possible with the information available at this stage.

This starts us thinking about the possibilities available for the design of the structure and is best indicated by an actual example of the procedures that our office went through to arrive at the required data on one project.

For IBM in Boulder, Colorado, the first requirement was a visit to the site to study the configuration of the land and adjacent terrain, to determine what utilities are available, to gauge the type and height of structures which would be consistent with the beauty of the vista and yet meet the very strict requirements of the client's budget limitations. The project included two manufacturing buildings, engineering building with laboratory facilities, power plant, and administration building. Client requirements dictated single-story construction for all except the administration building. Although the designers preferred a six-story administration building for better relationship to the site and the other buildings, it was decided to limit the height to three stories because of budget and operational limitations. The very rigid budget required extreme care in the choice of materials with which to build what is a substantial structure and, at the same time, achieve the desired appearance of the buildings.

Initially, brick and block walls and steel sash were to be used for the exterior surfaces, but when found that it was possible within the budget, the exterior wall was changed to exposed aggregate concrete construction. This was done after a very careful analysis and review, with two manufacturers of this material in the Denver area, of the type of wall desired for the architectural design. By following this procedure on all critical materials comprising a large portion of the project cost, we found that, after schematics, working drawings, and bidding, the total cost of the project came very close to the projected budget arrived at in the preschematic phase.

Cost Approximation in the Schematic Phase

Information to be determined in this phase, included:

1. Area of each floor and total area of the building
2. Quantities of all materials in the shell (architectural)
3. Quantities of structural material based on design of one bay, spread footings, basement walls

4. Site work
5. Number of elevators and costs
6. Number of hoists and costs
7. Group I furnishings and/or casework
8. Mechanical cost per square foot based on systems to be used
9. Electrical work cost per square foot based on systems to be used
10. Equipment (kitchen, etc.,) allowance
11. Contingency

Example of Approximate Quantity Takeoff

Area computation:

Area per floor: 100 × 100 ft	10,000 sq ft
10 floors: 10 × 10,000 ft	100,000 sq ft
Usable area	75,000 sq ft
Efficiency $\dfrac{75,000}{100,000}$	75 percent

Detail quantities:

Superstructure and walls: 4 × 100 = 400-ft periphery × 100 ft	40,000 sq ft
Assume sq ft proportions of:	
30,000 brick and block @ $4	$120,000
6,000 curtain wall @ $7	42,000
4,000 insulated glass @ $6	24,000
Excavation and backfill for basement	
(10,000 sq ft × 1½ cu yd per sq ft @ $2 cu yd)	30,000
Substructure walls: 4 × 100 = 400 × 16 ft = 6,400 sq ft @ $3	19,000
Footings, grade beams: 100,000 sq ft @ $0.50	50,000
Caissons: 500 cu yd @ $80	40,000
Sheet piling: 200 × 30 = 6,000 sq ft @ $7	42,000
Structural steel: 100,000 @ $1.60 (10 lb per sq ft @ $.16 per lb)	160,000
Concrete slab on ground: 10,000 sq ft @ $.80	8,000
Concrete, supporting floor: 100,000 sq ft @ $3.50	350,000
Miscellaneous metal: 3–5 percent of total building 90,000 to 150,000;	
use average	120,000
Fireproofing structural steel	30,000
Suspended ceiling: 90,000 sq ft @ $.80	72,000
Roofing, insulation and flashing: 10,000 sq ft @ $.60	6,000
Floor finishes: 100,000 sq ft @ $.50 average	50,000
Doors, hardware and frames: 300 @ $150	45,000
Stairs and railings: 2 stairs @ 190 treads = 380 treads = 1,600 lin ft	
plus 20 intermediate landings = 640 sq ft + 280 lin ft railing	24,000
Partitions: 100,000 @ $2.50	250,000
Painting: ceilings, partitions and inside of exterior walls = 440,000 sq ft	44,000
Miscellaneous: 3–5 percent of above	74,000
General conditions	200,000
Subtotal building work (100,000 sq ft @ $18)	$1,800,000

Example of Approximate Quantity Takeoff (continued)

Mechanical work: 100,000 sq ft @ $7.50 per sq ft	750,000
Electrical work: 100,000 sq ft @ $4.15 per sq ft	415,000
Elevators: 3 @ $70,000	210,000
Site: allowance	150,000
Removals: allowance	50,000
Subtotal	$3,375,000
Contingencies	325,000
Total	$3,700,000

The following are examples of several of our projects, with a brief history of each showing special features which can enter into the schematic phase of creative cost control.

High School—140,000 sq ft

We were given the maximum area and a maximum allowable cost of $16 per sq ft. This square-foot limitation meant that we could not exceed one story for most of the structure.

We had to use metal roof deck and insulation, short spans, brick and block exterior walls, and very economical partitions. We tried using longer spans where it was most desirable, but upon a schematic cost-control check we were required to back up and do considerable redesign. However, it is far better to back up at this stage than to face the task of doing over the entire project after the bids come in.

Factory, Laboratory, and Office Facility

We were given a maximum budget of $1,750,000 and an area of 55,000 sq ft, and it was mandatory that certain materials manufactured by subsidiaries of the client be used in the building.

Our schematic estimate indicated that the building would come in at 25 percent over the budget. The client was advised of this, but he was willing to proceed with bids and take a chance on their being favorable. When the bids came in unfavorably, redesign was necessary to cut the costs. We were able to keep the exterior design which we and client wanted, but had to do considerable redesign of other parts of the building to achieve the required economy.

Office Building

This building consisted of 472,000 sq ft in the final design. When the project began, the question was raised concerning the total number of stories. The designers preferred a twenty-eight- to thirty-five-story building, which would raise the cost considerably over the twenty stories first considered. This was discussed with the client, and it was decided to proceed with a twenty-eight-story building.

The schematic cost was estimated by our office. We had a check estimate made by two independent contractors, and our schematic estimate was verified within 3 to 5 percent. We were able to proceed with preliminary and final working drawings, and no cost difficulties were encountered during the rest of the project.

Office Building Complex

This complex consisted of the following structures: two-story, 2,000-car garage with approximately 435,000 sq ft of parking space per story, underneath and around two existing structures and three new buildings; three office buildings, including a four-story structure of about 220,000 sq ft, a seven-story structure with a two-story annex consisting of about 165,000 sq ft; and a four-story building of about 250,000 sq ft, to be developed by another architect but with our office having the responsibility for design and budget.

It was required that the budget be set approximately three years ahead of the time of construction. Appropriations were made in accordance with this budget, without any leeway. And the budget could not be exceeded. The cost per car was required to be a maximum of $2,300 for construction, in order to make the structure economically feasible. We could neither cut down the number of cars required, nor exceed the limits of the budget.

Total construction cost, a maximum of $27 per sq ft for the buildings, had to be maintained. This broke down as follows:

	$/sq ft
Building work	$15.30
Mechanical work	7.00
Electrical work	3.35
Elevators	1.00
Site	.35
Total	$27.00

The major trades were to be bid as separate primes with the successful general contractor's proposal including sufficient allowance to accept assignment of all the rest of the trades.

Although this was done three years ago, it turned out that we had followed the proper preschematic and schematic cost-control procedures, and the final results on the bidding were extremely satisfactory. All the extra effort has paid off, since bids are now in on approximately $15,000,000 work of construction on three of the four structures originally projected.

Federal Office Building

This example will tend to give an all-inclusive set of circumstances which takes a project from the beginning of the preschematic phase and carries it through the schematic, or tentative, phase.

The floor area of this structure had been set at 1,200,000 sq ft, with a budget limitation of $25,335,000 at the time of the negotiation of the contract between our office and GSA.

Cost control began in a Washington hotel room with the top men in our organization poring over a huge set of plans. It was questionable whether such a building could be built; it would have to be twenty-five or more stories high, on a very limited site which had already been secured, at a maximum cost of approximately $20 per sq ft. This figure would be possible for a two- or three-story office building on an adequate site, but in a metropolitan area, on a restricted site, it seemed like an impossible chore. This indicated the necessity for getting quantities of materials and costs per square foot at the very earliest possible stage.

The site was irregular in shape, similar to a twisted trapezoid, which prevented free use of all the space available on the site. There were principal streets around the periphery of the site, and major traffic arteries prevented continuous use for truck parking during delivery of concrete or other materials. It was possible that excavation would disclose boulders, old walls, rubble, and old foundations. It was certain that caissons would be required to a depth of 70 ft or more to get through blue clay to hardpan. Past experience indicated that delivery of materials to the site would be excluded by city ordinance during the rush hours—7:30 to 9:30 A.M. and 4 to 6 P.M. The building was to be finished in five years, from the date of negotiations.

The objective, of course, was a beautiful, monumental building of superior quality with an absolute budget limitation. Under similar circumstances, *before* an architect accepts a commission, he must start the cost-control procedures that will be required to keep within budget limitations.

Another requirement was that all materials to be used in all cases must follow the precepts of value engineering—this being understood to mean that if painted steel would give the desired results, aluminum, which costs considerably more per pound, would not be used. If aluminum could be used, stainless steel, which costs several times as much per pound, would not be used. These precepts were to be followed through the entire analysis of the preschematic and schematic cost approximations.

Our investigations developed a number of criteria such as those following:

1. If it were decided to use precast panels, they must be simple and economical and used in large enough quantities to achieve the economy of mass production. Wherever possible, insulation should be omitted on the interior of the precast panels. Precast panels should have a minimum of splays, convolutions, interfaces, and/or other shapes or forms that are difficult to fabricate and even more difficult to seal after erection.

2. Economical ceilings should be used, no metal pan ceilings if suspended plaster will suffice. Ceilings should be used only where absolutely required, such as in offices or corridors, for fireproofing, or to cover unsightly piping or utility ductwork. Ceilings should be omitted in utility spaces and elsewhere, if possible.

3. If structural steel frame, spray-on fireproofing should be used, not fireproofing with concrete, which requires both reinforcing and form work and which adds a great deal of weight to the structure, thereby increasing the cost.

4. The structural layout and the framing should be as simple as possible for the greatest economy; i.e., cantilevers kept to a minimum and a system used that will give greatest economy of materials and lightest weight to keep columns to a minimum size in order to get the maximum possible amount of usable space.

5. Smallest spans permissible should be used within the module determined for the use of the entire structure.

6. Modular size should be used to attain the minimum amount of core space. This will result in more usable space and will achieve greatest efficiency in the use of the building.

7. Use the minimum amount of efficient vertical transportation. Elevators are very expensive on twenty- to thirty-story buildings.

Mechanical Work

Systems should be designed for the greatest economy to meet the allowable cost. This economy can be achieved by use of some of the following practices:

1. Minimum sheet-metal thickness, to the limits of good practice

2. Strap hangers for support of ductwork instead of much heavier angles

3. One window heating unit for every two or three modules rather than one unit per module

4. Minimum thickness of duct insulation and no insulation on cold-air ducts and/or other places where it is not absolutely required

5. Good, but economical, toilet fixtures

6. Minimum possible number of zones for air conditioning, the whole mechanical heating system to be predicated upon the use of central heat furnished by a utility company, therefore requiring no boiler plant

Electrical Work

Economy should be attained in the electrical system by avoiding the use of eggcrate ceiling, the very highest-quality lighting fixtures, or an excessive number of footcandles, none of which can be justified by amount allowed for electrical work. Client requirements should not be exceeded either in the number of footcandles furnished or in the quality of fixtures specified.

Elevators

The population of the building, 5,000 people, requires a minimum of sixteen elevators. We can get by with eighteen elevators if we use two freight and sixteen high-speed, gearless elevators, with some of these handling only certain lower floors and the required number going to all floors. Escalators are too expensive for this structure.

Miscellaneous

Omit window-washing equipment; omit escalators; use good, but economical, windows.

The intention of the discussion above is to stress the use of creative cost control in such a way that all the ingenuity of all the designers is put to work to achieve an outstanding building within the budget, thus deriving quality from excellent design rather than from the use of expensive materials, intricate details of construction, and elaborate systems.

For this project, the client requirements shaped up like this:

Maximum budget	$25,335,000
Area of building required	1,200,000 sq ft
Area of site available	107,000 sq ft

Since the client's requirements for space, budget, and site area available for building were all very critical and confining, we had to determine the minimum cost to provide the required space.

In order to obtain a tower design, we assumed the dimensions as close to a square as possible and, therefore, started in the following way.

If we have two levels of basement, of 107,000 sq ft each, using the entire area to the property line, we will have available 1,200,000 sq ft less the 214,000 sq ft of basement, or 986,000 sq ft for the office tower. 986,000 sq ft divided by eighteen floors = 54,600 sq ft per floor. The square root of the area of a single floor equals 233 ft. Therefore, we would have a tower consisting of eighteen stories each 12 ft high, for a total height of 216 ft above ground. Thus, the dimensions of our structure would be 233 × 233 × 216 ft above ground.

We assumed the following for the structure:

1. 20 × 20 ft as the size of the bay.

2. The exterior wall to be simple and flat precast.

3. The windows to be lightweight aluminum sash with sheet glass.

4. The structural frame to be concrete joists and slab on structural steel or concrete—which to be determined by future analysis.

5. Heating and power will be furnished by a power company, so that no boiler plant will be required.

6. No escalators or window-washing equipment.

7. No underfloor ducts.

The next step was to develop a rough estimate of the cost of such a structure by means of a conference call between our top-level team in Washington and all our department heads in Detroit. In the table following is an example of our prenegotiation cost approximation.

COST APPROXIMATION NO. 1 *Federal Office Building*
(Eighteen-story superstructure +
two-story substructure = twenty stories)

1. Removals, caissons and excavation	$ 500,000
2. Slab on ground—107,000 sq ft	100,000
3. Basement slab—107,000 sq ft @ $3	321,000
4. First floor and roof over basement 107,000 × sq ft @ $5.00	535,000
5. Second floor through eighteenth floor—986,000 sq ft	3,000,000
6. Structural steel 1,200,000 sq ft @ $3.20 (Assume 20 lb per sq ft @ .16 per lb = $3.20)	3,800,000
7. Walls below grade = 43,000 sq ft @ $5 (1359 × 32 = 43,000 sq ft)	215,000
8. Precast exterior walls (simple and flat) 210,000 sq ft @ $4.00 (233 × 4 = 932 ft × 216 ft high = 210,000 sq ft)	840,000
9. Aluminum sash (lightweight) standard fixed, with sheet glass 105,000 sq ft @ $3.50	360,000
10. Roofing	70,000
11. Suspended ceilings: assume 1,000,000 sq ft	700,000
12. Floor finish: vinyl asbestos—assume 800,000 sq ft	320,000
13. Steel stud and concrete-block partitions 1,200,000 sq ft @ $1.00	1,200,000
14. Assume 1,000 hollow metal doors and aluminum exterior doors	180,000
15. Lobby	100,000
16. Elevator lobby: 30,000 sq ft vinyl	30,000
17. General conditions for building and structural work	1,200,000
Total, building and structural work	$13,471,000
Elevators (sixteen and two service), assume	1,450,000
Cafeteria equipment (per client), assume	110,000
Mechanical work: 1,000,000 sq ft @ $4.50, 200,000 @ $3	5,100,000
Electrical work: 1,200,000 sq ft @ $2.25 (no underfloor duct)	2,700,000
Sitework: assume	300,000
General conditions: Items 2 to 6 inclusive	1,000,000
Contingency	1,200,000
Total construction cost	$25,331,000

Our next step was to develop a comparison of floor areas, floor dimensions, heights of superstructure, and areas of superstructure walls of buildings ranging from eighteen to thirty stories in height. These were compared with cost, as indicated in the table following.

COST APPROXIMATION NO. 2   *Federal Office Building*
(Comparison of eighteen-versus-twenty-four-story superstructure, both with two-story substructures)

		18-*story* superstructure	24-*story* superstructure
1.	Caissons, excavation, etc.	$ 500,000	$ 500,000
2.	Slab on ground	100,000	100,000
3.	Basement slab	321,000	321,000
4.	First floor and roof over basement	535,000	535,000
5.	Superstructure concrete	2,940,000	2,940,000
6.	Structural steel	3,820,000	4,760,000
7.	Walls below grade	215,000	215,000
8.	Superstructure walls	840,000	890,000
9.	Sash	360,000	390,000
10.	Roofing	70,000	64,000
11.	Suspended ceiling	700,000	700,000
12.	Floor finish	320,000	320,000
13.	Partitions	1,200,000	1,200,000
14.	Doors	180,000	180,000
15.	Lobby	200,000	200,000
16.	Elevation lobby	30,000	30,000
17.	General conditions	1,230,000	1,335,000
	Total, building and structural work	$13,561,000	$14,680,000
	Elevator	1,420,000	1,420,000
	Cafeteria equipment (per client)	110,000	110,000
	Mechanical work	5,100,000	5,200,000
	Electrical work	3,220,000	3,220,000
	Sitework	300,000	300,000
	General conditions: Items 2 to 6 inclusive	1,150,000	1,200,000
	Contingency	1,239,000	1,300,000
	Total construction cost	$26,100,000	$27,430,000

In order to arrive at structural-steel costs for the schematics, we prepared charts (in pounds per square foot) as in Fig. 12.1, for different bay sizes. The bay sizes were based on a 4 ft 8 in. module, the most satisfactory for the client's requirements and for our proposed design. These charts gave us pounds of steel per square foot for structures from eighteen to thirty-four stories in height. We then made a more accurate chart, as in Fig. 12.2, of structural steel weights per square foot for only bay sizes of 23 ft 4 in. and 28 ft square. A chart, as in Fig. 12.3, was then made of three bay sizes in order to arrive at the sizes of the columns required, if the entire structural frame were reinforced concrete.

The foregoing will serve only to give some indication of the detail

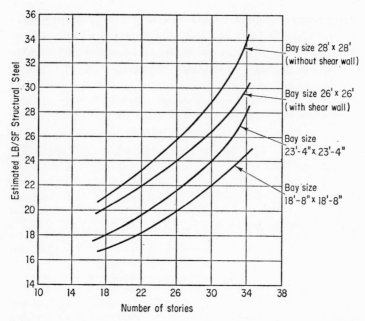

Note:

Estimation based on following:
  Detroit building code
  Horizontal drift control 0.0025h
  Welded rigid-frame construction
  Two-way concrete slab
  A-36 steel
  L.L. 60 #/$_\square$'
  Spray-on fireproofing

FIG. 12.1   *Structural steel estimate no. 1.*

and care required to establish and maintain cost control of buildings as early as possible, even before negotiations actually begin between the architects and their potential client.

Although not feasible in the preceding case of the Federal office building, it is often satisfactory, in the preschematic phase, to use cost per square foot, or cost per cubic foot, in order to get an extremely rough idea of the budget. However, after the preschematic phase, it is important that approximations be made of the quantities of materials required.

Schematic estimates must be realistic. There may be a temptation to keep estimates low, but this can lead to bitter disappointment when the bids come in. And it is possible to arrive at an approximation of the quantity of materials required for a project even at its very earliest stage in order to determine its probable cost and feasibility.

When comparisons are made for the purposes of cost control, every element of them must be made completely valid. For example, size must be considered when comparing one building with a theoretically similar structure—a 100,000 sq ft hospital may cost $30 to $45 per sq ft but a 500,000 sq ft hospital can be built at a cost of $27 to $33 per sq ft. The form of building determines the amount of its exterior walls, as well as the exposure for heating, ventilating and air conditioning, and the amount of daylight and artificial lighting. Long narrow buildings are relatively more expensive than ones that are more square, and, unless necessary for function or design, should be avoided. Many bulges or odd shapes in a building are in the same category, and will add greatly to the budget.

The height of a building affects the cost of the structure required to resist wind and earthquakes, the cost of elevators, the cost for lost time in lifting materials and men, and other items.

Space allocations for mechanical work must be adequate. If the form of the building limits the freedom of air movement and causes too many

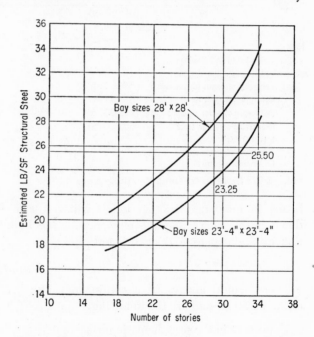

Note:
Estimation based on following:
Detroit building code
Horizontal drift control 0.0025h
Welded rigid-frame construction
Two-way concrete slab
A-36 steel
L.L. 60 $^\#/_\square{}'$
Spray-on fireproofing

FIG. 12.2 *Structural steel estimate no. 2.*

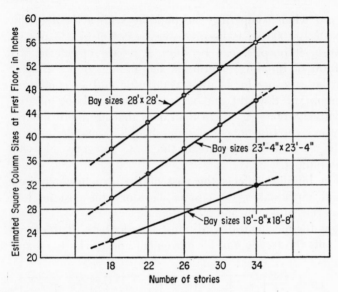

FIG. 12.3 *Reinforced concrete column estimate.*

bends in ductwork, friction losses will result in larger ducts, cutting down usable space and the efficiency of the building and will require difficult and expensive ductwork and piping.

Variation of Contingency

There should always be a contingency attached in every budget or estimate. Suggested are the following:

15 percent in the preschematic phase
10 to 12 percent in the schematic phase
5 to 8 percent in the preliminary phase
3 to 5 percent in the working-drawing phase

Requirements for Cost Control

It is necessary to keep good and accurate cost records. In our office, we actually prepare cost indices as shown in Fig. 12.4. This requires a

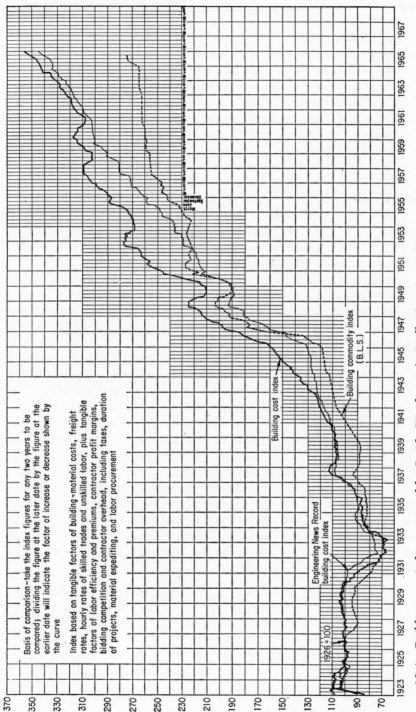

Basis of comparison—take the index figures for any two years to be compared; dividing the figure at the later date by the figure of the earlier date will indicate the factor of increase or decrease shown by the curve

Index based on tangible factors of building-material costs, freight rates, hourly rates of skilled trades and unskilled labor, plus tangible factors of labor efficiency and premiums, contractor profit margins, bidding competition and contractor overhead, including taxes, duration of projects, material expediting, and labor procurement

1926 = 100

Engineering News Record building cost index

Building cost index

Building commodity index (B.L.S.)

March and September and December

FIG. 12.4 *Building cost index, prepared by Smith, Hinchman & Grylls, Associates, Inc.*

187

great deal of continuous research into the condition of the general economy throughout the country. It is necessary to keep an eye on business conditions and to watch for sudden drops in any sector that may cause costs to decrease. By the same token, it is also necessary to look for all signs of booming sectors that will result in cost increases. Trade journals and cost indices by contractors and government agencies should be checked for decreases or increases, in order to keep up to date.

Data should be secured for regional variations as published by various agencies. But these published items should be carefully scrutinized for the possibility that the bench marks used in them are not appropriate for all locations.

The cost index, prepared in our office, is based on labor rates, material prices and freight rates, productivity of labor, efficiency of plant and management, competitive conditions, material prices, subcontractors' unit prices, and general contractors' fees.

For our index, we review and adjust prices on the basis of contractors' bids received on projects throughout the United States. Whenever possible, we secure actual unit prices in the prevailing area. There are too many variations for an exact formula, and, therefore, our building index is also based on judgment and experience.

Architects should build up-to-date and continuing files of unit prices of all trades in as great detail as possible. A prime requisite in this is knowledge of what contractors include for "general conditions," for "overhead," for "profit allowances," and for "miscellaneous." Also, it is necessary to conduct continuous research in use of materials, comparative advantage of materials, economic conditions, competitive conditions, regional differences in costs and use of materials, and labor availability (skilled and common, union and nonunion).

For proper cost control, the file should include unit costs of materials erected in place to use for approximate takeoffs of materials. These units should be checked against contractors' unit costs obtained from time to time on specific projects. Our office has kept a unit-cost file and published its cost index for more than fifty years.

Checklist of Possible Traps

When a project is in the schematic phase, the architect should visit the site and secure knowledge of the underground conditions. This knowledge should include items such as the following:

1. Site survey
2. Rural or metropolitan location of the site
3. Accessibility to the site by truck or railroad

4. Site size limitations or restrictions

5. Room for contractors' storage of materials on standby trucks

6. City ordinances prohibiting or regulating rush-hour delivery

7. Possibility of boulders, old walls, or rubble being encountered during excavation

8. Water conditions requiring pumping

9. Shoring or underpinning of adjacent structure

10. Requirements of all applicable codes

11. Requirements of utility companies

12. Competitive conditions in the area

13. Overtime conditions in the area

14. Electrical workers' wage rates

15. Mileage expense for mechanics brought beyond certain zones, such as 10 miles from city hall

16. Government restrictions, such as GSA's requirements for listing of contractors and subcontractors with proposal

Checklist of General Requirements

Cost control is affected by many things such as:

1. Bidding one general contract with central responsibility versus five or six primes with no provision for assignment

2. Negotiated contract with management fee and a top limit

3. Prebids for long-lead items which may cause confusion and great difficulty in coordinating a project

4. Two sets of inspectors (client's and architect's) with no definition of authority. (Such divided responsibility causes delays and increases costs.)

5. Availability of local materials

6. Custom-made versus standard-stock items

7. Use of materials, such as steel, if a major strike is on and termination is not in sight

8. Availability of skilled labor

9. Union or nonunion labor

10. Labor market. (If forty hours is a standard week, add 10 to 25 percent if shortages of labor require that contractors give employees 50, 55, 60 or even more hours a week.)

Items Causing High Proposals

This office has found that failure to adhere to the following procedures can cause contractors to raise prices. They are therefore very important in keeping costs down:

1. Allow as much time as possible to construct the project or give the bidders the option of setting the time required.

2. Avoid restrictive specifications limiting the number of bidders, e.g., using the same supplier's name so frequently that bidders get the feeling that only one supplier is acceptable.

3. Do not limit the requirements for concrete aggregate, cement, or stone to one quarry unless the client is aware of this and is willing to pay a premium for limiting the competition.

4. Do not restrict concrete pouring to daylight hours, but leave this up to the contractor.

5. Do not tell the contractor to use steel forms of a certain weight, if it is permissible to use any type of forms.

6. Use premanufactured forms, if possible, of cardboard or other economical materials.

7. Do not use double-lined forms when single forms will serve.

8. Do not restrict form stripping unless this is necessary to get the desired effect.

9. Limit waterproofing to what is required.

10. If the budget is very limited, use a slab on ground rather than a slab with vapor barrier, 4-in. fill, dampproofing, and perimeter insulation.

11. Do not use a concrete slab and a waterproofing concrete slab, if concrete and waterproofing will suffice.

12. Temporary heat should be in the mechanical work.

13. Temporary wiring should be in the electrical work.

14. Give sufficient information to clearly define mechanical systems or equipment.

15. Review mechanical specifications to eliminate outdated equipment.

16. Watch for substitution of items causing cost differentials.

17. Check sequence of mechanical work as related to other trades.

18. Avoid conflicting requirements for mechanical equipment.

19. Give proper consideration to clearances between piping and ductwork.

20. Schedule sequence of work to avoid excessive temporary heat.

21. Do not limit competition on light fixtures, switch gear, and substation and control equipment.

22. Avoid acceptance tests which exceed normal requirements.

23. Do not require extravagant temporary electric power.

PART FIVE

*Maintaining
Control until
Building Completion*

THIRTEEN

Bernard J. Grad, FAIA

Control during Design Development

The design development phase presents, perhaps, the greatest challenge of all to the cost-conscious architect. It has been compared with a Camp Parents' Day type of race wherein the contestant is given a raw egg on a spoon and told to traverse an obstacle course with the egg unbroken. The fragile egg in this case is the budget—established at the beginning of the architect's services—which must be preserved intact despite many obstacles. The successful architect is one who can come through this phase with the estimated cost of the project still within the established budget.

Our firm has developed procedures to maintain close surveillance of project costs during the design development phase. Creative cost control is the method—with the emphasis on control. The following will be an examination of procedures employed.

Before outlining the methods used in this cost-control process, it would be best to review what is to be accomplished during this phase of project development. The design development phase involves the translating of the schematic outline of a project into a more fully defined and organized statement. More accurate analyses are made of the basic circulation patterns, interrelationships of spaces, exact siting of the building or buildings, access and egress for personnel and materials, and the structural, mechanical, and electrical systems. A specification outlining and defining all construction materials, methods, and systems is prepared. Based upon these investigations, a *definitive design* is arrived at in all these areas. The result is an exact definition of the project design, with the details of all phases of the work now developed.

General assumptions and basic system designations made during the schematic phase must now be defined and positively stated in the design development phase. This "firming-up" process and the requirements for an exact statement of intent cause this stage of a project to be *most critical* in respect to cost control. Having established their cost goals in the previous phase, architects must now exercise all possible diligence to maintain their goals.

At the end of this phase the result will be a set of plans, specifications, and a cost estimate which clearly and accurately define and detail the entire project. Upon the approval of these documents, they will be turned over to the architects' production team to produce the final working drawings and specifications for bidding and building purposes.

The Challenge

Given a well-defined set of schematic documents and a realistic budget, why does the design development phase still present such a challenge to the architect regarding costs? The answer, most simply stated, is that this is the "creep" stage. Every general decision previously made must now be translated into specific procedures, and each contains the possibility of opening another door to increased cost. An examination of the factors militating against cost control, which require the architect's continuous close attention, demonstrates the wide scope of the problems and why this stage of development is termed the creep stage.

Improved Client Understanding

During this stage, the owner becomes more aware, through continued contact with his architects and through further graphic presentations of the project which he has already approved in the schematic stage, of what the project really includes. To expect a client to visualize a total concept from the schematic documents is unrealistic. At this time, the client starts requesting additional items or modifications of those he has already approved. Especially is this true of large corporate or governmental clients which tend to be segmented and stratified, requiring approvals on many different levels by a variety of persons of different backgrounds, each with his own visualization of the drawings presented by the architects. Each of the client's department heads, reacting to the additional details now introduced and based on his correspondingly better understanding, usually contributes additional ideas based on individual knowledge and experience which, even when valid, could have an adverse influence on the maintenance of a defined cost.

The acceptance of these new ideas while, at the same time, controlling costs represents a real challenge to the architects—whose experience and background must now be brought into play to evaluate these ideas in the light of the total project program and costs. The architects' role now is to maintain an atmosphere in which they can reason together with their clients for the maximum benefit of the project.

An example of what can happen in this respect occurred recently in a college science-building project which was well into the design development stage, having previously received approval from all departments. The chemistry department members suddenly "discovered" that what was being planned for them really was not what they had expected. After much analysis and debate, it became necessary to increase the program to accommodate these new ideas and to set up a corresponding increase in the budget.

On more complex projects, involving many disciplines, this type of "discovery" by lay people unskilled in the art of visualization is almost inevitable. The most positive way of offsetting this problem—or at least limiting it—is to provide the client, in the early phases of the project, with as much graphic and descriptive material as is possible; this will aid him in the visualization and understanding of what he is buying for his money. Our firm has found that extra time and effort spent in sketches, renderings, and models in the early stages of a project go a long way toward obviating the need for major revisions at a later date.

Defining and Refining of Function

As each area and component of the building is scrutinized and finalized, many aspects of project requirements previously half-hidden under the veil of generality become more clearly defined. A stairway, previously indicated only as a series of parallel lines, now will have materials selected for tread and riser, handrail and balusters, etc. It is only natural that the architects will want to create the best for their clients, and in turn, the client will want to have the best.

Throughout this stage the architects are forced to decisions in their selection of materials and in the development of the details of the functional design. What is best for the project? Will saving money at this stage mean a false economy with higher maintenance costs a result? Painted block or plaster? Terrazzo or resilient tile? Stainless steel or aluminum? Throughout this process of definition and development, the architects must keep a scorecard of building costs, because it is here that the battle of creeping cost must be fought with the tools of experience and understanding.

The likelihood of increasing the building area beyond that which was approved in the schematics is also a factor which must be carefully guarded against. As areas are detailed—with subfunctions and equipment finally indicated—there is a natural tendency to enlarge the area of the building. Again the designers' vigilance must be put to the test.

In the design state of a medical building, as large block areas labeled laboratories, x-ray department and physical therapy department are broken down into actual working layouts requiring corridors and equipment, it takes all the architects' ingenuity and creative ability to come up with a solution including all functional requirements—without increasing the building area.

Defining the Unknown

Just as everyone's fingerprints are unique, so every project involving an individual company will have features which are the reflections of the company's own products and individual approach to producing its products. Each large corporation or government agency has its own approach to the use of public spaces. The type and size of kitchen and cafeteria can vary greatly. Toilet areas and lobby sizes are designed differently for different clients. Aspects such as the amount of parking, width of corridors, lighting levels, air conditioning, sound attenuation, sun control, and many other elements in the design of a building complex vary greatly for different clients. Another large variable aspect is the exposed materials, which can help create an image of wealth, austerity, etc. It must be the responsibility of the architects, while defining the schematic program, to ferret out all the individual idiosyncrasies of their clients in these aspects—and all of them will reflect themselves in the cost of the buildings.

One recent large industrial client insisted that he wanted only air cooling (instead of air conditioning) just to make the employees aware of a movement of air while keeping costs low. Contrast that with a recent project in which our office was required to provide a HVAC system with very fine temperature and humidity control to ensure happy employees in a highly competitive and labor-short industry.

One corporation requested an expensive-appearing exterior in its corporate headquarters to emphasize the success and position it had obtained. Another even larger client insisted on economical-appearing finishes to stress to its stockholders and clients its competitive position through frugality in its building program.

This wide range of approach—from pipe rack to palace—with the many possible variations in between must be defined, and agreed to, before the exact scope of a project can be determined.

Rising Building Costs

Inevitably the cost of building continues to rise. This problem is especially critical when the design development period becomes extended beyond its normal length. Realistic contingencies must be written into the schematic budget to reflect the project development time and possible increases in cost. Should the project continue, for any reason, beyond the anticipated period of development, the impact of increased costs for this additional period must be evaluated.

The *Wall Street Journal* recently described the experience of the Bay Area Rapid Transit District in San Francisco which in 1962, while budgeting its costs for a new rapid-transit system to be completed in 1971, figured costs would rise by 21 percent. By 1966, costs had already risen 21 percent. The budgeters had assumed that construction wage costs would rise 3 percent a year, but in fact they have risen much faster—5 percent last year alone. In addition, material prices keep rising throughout the country.

Meeting the Challenge

Our office has developed specific techniques which result in the protection of the client and the project through the control of the cost of construction during the critical design development phase.

At the inception of a project, a project team is created under the direction of a partner or an associate and under the leadership of a project manager. This team includes a representative of each of the consulting engineers, the specification writer, and the firm's cost-control manager. After defining the program, through preliminaries and a realistic budget estimate, the next responsibility of the project team is to create the building within the established cost. Their efforts end with the award of the construction contract—within the budget.

After approval of schematics, this team meets periodically to review all aspects of the project, including the total cost. One responsibility of the project team is to make sure that the owner *understands what he is approving*. The better the client's recognition of the scope of the work, the better the chance of forestalling later cost increases through his later "discovery" of the project content.

At the end of the schematic phase, our organization, using such graphic tools as rendered plans, circulation-flow diagrams, furniture and equipment layouts, renderings, and models, attempts to convey to the client an understanding of the project. Because these presentation meetings are held with all levels of organization, the important element of conveying to everyone the *same* understanding of the project is stressed.

Quite often, these review meetings will indicate that the client's program is inconsistent with his budget—resulting in a necessary change in budget or program. It is only through this sort of *careful analysis* and *mutual understanding* that inconsistencies in the budget and program can be discovered and solutions realized.

Typical of this type of exchange is what happened in a recent project which included a classroom and science building at a large university. The program, which was presented to us by the client, included 44,000 sq ft of net usable space, with an added allowance of 25 percent of that area, or 11,000 sq ft, for nonassignable areas such as circulation spaces and toilets. The total gross area required was 55,000 sq ft.

In addition, a fixed budget amount was established. Our review of this budget indicated that 55,000 gross sq ft could be built for the budgeted amount. However, from our experience with this type of building in the past, we knew that for a gross area of 55,000 sq ft, there must be allocated approximately 19,000 sq ft of nonassignable area, leaving a net area of 36,000 sq ft in lieu of the 44,000 established by the client.

Something had to give—either an increase in the budget or a reduction in the net area. The funds allocated could not be increased, and therefore, it was necessary to restudy the requirements for net area to reduce the figure from the 44,000 sq ft originally required to the 36,000 sq ft which the budget allowed. By careful scrutiny of all spaces and discussions with the various department heads, we were able to reduce the net area to the allowable 36,000 sq ft, which when added to the 19,000 nonassignable area, gave a total of 55,000 sq ft. The result—the bid came in less than one percent below the budget, and the project is now under construction. Happy client—and happy architect.

Once a project proceeds into the design development phase, we require that the client appoint his own team (preferably an individual or a maximum of three persons) who will remain as the contact with our office through the development of the entire project. *Communication* between these two groups becomes of prime importance to the continued mutual understanding of both parties during this period.

Similarly, periodic meetings of the production team enable it to identify any creeping design items which are worked into the project during the design development phase. Any new item—unanticipated in the establishment of the budget—is now analyzed for its necessity in the project as well as for its effect on the total project cost.

Examples of the type of review, discussion, and decision making which take place during this phase cover a wide range. For example, the cost of raising the ground-floor level of a large manufacturing plant by 1 ft was more than offset by sharply reduced costs in site grading and utility distribution because of rock on the site. It also provided the entrance and appearance which the designers wanted.

In another case, a study was made of the cost effects of projecting columns as sun-control devices and the use of tinted glass (both higher-cost items) as compared with lowered heating and air-conditioning costs. Also, alternate wall sections can be cost evaluated and a selection made based upon the results of such comparisons.

One parking-garage study indicated that a precast-concrete scheme would be some $24,000 less than a poured-in-place scheme for this particular building.

All materials and methods were examined in an effort to assure lower cost through such means as simplicity of details; use of stock materials; use of as few trades as possible; proper scheduling of trades—so that a trade would not be required to return to complete a job after another trade had performed its work; multiple use of items; repetitive use of items; use of shop-fabricated items in lieu of field-fabricated; use of local materials, not requiring high shipping and handling costs; limiting the use of scaffolding, shoring, underpinning, pumping, etc; and many other areas.

Constant evaluation and analysis takes place in the firming up of a project. Writing the outline specification exposes to the light of scrutiny various alternatives for materials and methods. Further, the outline specification forces decisions and firm definition of all aspects of the work. Thus, the outline specification becomes the definitive document for the production of the project and is used as the basis for the final specification which is sent out to the bidders. A sample section of an outline specification is shown here.

    H. Toilet rooms and janitors closets
       1. Floors—nonslip, porcelain type, cushion edge mosaic unglazed tile
       2. Walls—glazed interior wall tile, cushion edge; full height in toilet rooms and base only in janitors' closets
       3. Hung ceilings—Keene's cement plaster
       4. Toilet room accessories in men's and women's toilet rooms
       5. Toilet rooms—ceiling-hung flush-type metal toilet partitions
    I. Metal furring and lathing
       1. $1 \times \frac{3}{16}$-in. strap hangers for hung plaster ceilings
       2. No. 8 wire hangers for suspended acoustical tile ceilings

    3. 2-in. cold rolled channels (main runners—plaster).
    4. 1½-in. cold rolled channels (main runners—acoustical)
    5. ¾-in. channels—cross furring
 J. Glass and glazing
    1. Exterior—¼-in. thick, heat-absorbing, gray-tinted polished plate glass except south elevation of museum basement
    2. Basement—¼-in. thick, polished plate glass, glazing quality
    3. Interior—⁷⁄₃₂-in. thick obscure glass and ¼-in. thick polished plate glass, glazing quality
    4. Glass sealant—liquid polymer silicone rubber
 K. Finish hardware
    1. Hinges—1½ pair all doors
    2. Floor closures—entrance and vestibule doors
    3. Push and pull plates—stainless-steel exterior doors and doors to toilet rooms
    4. Overhead closures—interior corridor and stair doors
    5. Flush bolts—inactive leaf on pairs of doors
    6. Locksets—heavy-duty, cylindrical key-in-knob
    7. Bumpers—for all doors, except those with closures
    8. Finish—U.S. 32D (satin stainless steel)

The writing of this document reveals to the designers unanticipated features of the project which will affect the cost. Another tool our firm uses in controlling costs during this stage is the maintenance of a limit on the area of the project. Keeping within this limit further assures us of keeping within the established cost.

Further Definition of Cost

Toward the end of the design development phase, when definitive drawings and an outline specification have been prepared, a new estimate of cost is made. In the schematic phase, the estimator could only apply unit-cost-per-square-foot figures along with lump-sum allowances in establishing the budget, and then apply a contingency figure. At the end of the design development phase, enough information will be available for more precise quantity takeoffs. The estimator now may approach the job as a total entity, using the total costs of all elements rather than extensions of a typical unit (such as a cost of a typical building bay times the total number of bays). Factors that will affect the bidding process can be weighed, including the season during which the building will be built (e.g., it costs more to excavate and pour concrete in cold weather), size of the quantities involved (the larger the job, the lower the unit cost), the type of bidding anticipated (the more *interested* the bidders, the lower the price), the effects of new materials or methods of construction on labor-union jurisdictions (e.g., items such as radiant acoustic ceilings which combine heat with ceiling structure with illumination).

This takeoff is now recorded on estimating sheets, such as that in Fig. 14.1. As much detail as possible should be included. All items that have been frozen are now identified, measured, and evaluated.

In addition to the material takeoff, general conditions items, such as insurance, financing, watchmen, construction shanty, fencing, protection, all items of overhead (telephone, secretary, etc.), plus probable contractor profits, are listed. General conditions forms listing all probable items in this category are prepared.

In cases where a unique application of existing materials or new methods are envisioned, advice is sought from general contractors, subcontractors, manufacturers, or union officials, in order to establish the best and most efficient manner to detail and to evaluate costs.

Added at the end of each cost statement is a contingency factor, established separately for each project. While the cost estimate itself is an evaluation of what is known about a project, the contingency factor is a device to protect against the unknown. Therefore, the contingency amount will depend on the scope of definition of the project available at the time of the estimate. The contingency element at this stage may vary from 5 percent up to 20 percent.

Various governmental agencies require differing contingency factors during this stage of development. For example, the New York State University Construction Fund requires 15 percent contingency at the schematic stage, 10 percent contingency at the "Design Manual" stage (design development phase), and 5 percent in the final estimate. One district office of the Corps of Engineers requests that a contingency of $7\frac{1}{2}$ percent be applied at the design development stage.

When the contingency factor has been applied and the various sums totaled, a statement of *probable construction cost* has been achieved. In addition to this total amount, breakdowns for site work, general construction, and mechanical and electric work should be established. Each division should be listed in total cost and in cost per gross square foot so that these figures may be compared with the figures established at the schematic stage.

Further, this statement of cost should list the items not included in this accounting, but which are, even so, factors to be considered by the client in his establishing the total project cost. These additional items would include, for example, land cost, architect's fees, construction-inspection staff, filing fees, new equipment and furniture costs, and moving expenses. It is further advisable to include a statement relating the estimated costs to the *Engineering News-Record* building index or other established cost indices.

Review and Adjustment

After the establishment of the probable construction cost, a meeting is held to review the figures. The new figures are compared with the schematic estimate, and any major variations are investigated for the reasons causing the changes. Analyses are made to determine whether the original figures were valid assumptions in the light of the increased information now available. If the original figures are still considered reasonable, various alternatives are explored to discover whether the new figure could be reduced by substitution of less expensive materials or methods of construction. It is at this point that painted concrete-block partitions may be substituted for plaster, or aluminum entrances for stainless steel, etc. After the review is made and revisions determined, the preliminary set of drawings, outline specifications, and cost estimate are revised to indicate these decisions. The formal presentation of the documents may then be made.

Presentation to the Client

Presentation of the cost estimate to the client may be made in person or through the mail. Government and corporate clients, with segmented areas of responsibility, usually require submission in writing in accordance with standard forms.

Most architects prefer to make this presentation in person. Since the costs should be related to the project from which they are developed, it is best to present all aspects of the project *including costs* as a total package. At a meeting with responsible client representatives, the total development can be outlined along with the thought that went into its formation. The cost is then introduced in proper context, and the ensuing discussion can result in an exchange of ideas between the architect and his client.

Should the new estimate exceed the client's previous budget, explanations of and comparisons with the previous analyses and evaluations can be made. At this time, the owner may be willing to reduce the cost by accepting alternatives not previously recognized or accepted. This open airing of the subject, with the full design development package available for examination, should lead to a greater mutual understanding of problems and desires regarding the project, and it should make for more intelligent solutions that will be acceptable to both architect and client. The approval of the documents at this stage then establishes a much better basis for the further development of the project.

The architect enters the design development phase with a schematic package, including a budget. His challenge then is to define, more exactly, the myriad components of the project within the broad-brush definition of its scope and cost as originally established. His tools are *background, experience,* and *knowledge* of materials and methods of construction and their costs. Important elements in this process are *good communications* with his consultants and his clients and *sound judgment* to identify and evaluate the factors which will probably affect the future construction cost. Admittedly, elements of crystal-ball gazing and luck are involved at this stage, but most importantly, an organization of competent people is the key factor—for what happens at this stage will affect the life of both client and architect for the remainder of the project.

FOURTEEN

Irvin L. Timlin

Control during Construction Document Preparation

The estimating of building costs during the working-drawing, or construction-document, phase of architectural and engineering services is concerned with the determination of the third of the three construction variables—size, quality, cost.

The project started with a program based on the needs of the client. The first variable, the building size, is a direct result of the needed area plus circulation and other secondary areas.

The second variable, quality, has been determined by the client's requirements for interior finishes, structural system, and other design elements during the preliminary stages.

The third variable, cost, is a direct result of the above.

The only method of determining the cost of a structure with any degree of accuracy is to make a detailed takeoff of each item within the structure. An assumption that a project is a typical building, similar to one bid several years ago in a distant city, or an average building ranging halfway between the national average of high and low building prices published in a trade journal, is only, at best, a *guess,* not an estimate. The architect has often been accused, in the past, of guesses, of making his estimates "on the back of an envelope."

Today, the architect must present his client with realistic cost control, *not* intended as a guarantee of building cost, but intended to produce a building that meets the requirements of the client in space, function, and *budget.*

Cost control, at the working-drawing stage, is an expensive function requiring a major investment on the part of an architectural office. On the other hand, this cost can be more than offset by the extremely high cost of revising or redrawing a complete project in the event that it exceeds the budget.

The basic function of an architect, in this area of his work, is to establish a budget jointly with the client and to prepare a set of working drawings which will meet the requirements of the client and still stay within the limits of the budget.

The architect who can consistently meet these requirements should have little difficulty in acquiring future commissions. In starting an estimate at this stage, the use of the sixteen divisions outlined in the *Uniform System for Construction Specifications, Data Filing and Cost Accounting* (a joint publication of AIA, AGC, CSI, and CMSCI) is a very good method for classification of materials and procedures.

The actual takeoff of quantities should be performed by a person who is familiar with building construction and architectural and structural products, and who has the ability to read and understand drawings and specifications. The actual multiplication may be done with a slide rule or a calculator, totaling items to an even-dollar figure. It is unrealistic to work beyond three decimals or to carry any total beyond the even-dollar amount because many of the factors involved cannot be gauged to this degree of accuracy.

By working with even amounts, the estimator can keep his mind free to use his best judgment and common sense instead of becoming involved in a mass of computations. Keeping in mind a clear picture of the overall project will allow the estimator to make a *check* of each division within the estimate. An example of a *check* of a detailed estimate is outlined in the following paragraphs.

A rectangular building, two stories high, 98 ft. × 211 ft. 6 in., with concrete-frame construction would have a total square footage of 41,454. Rounding the total square footage to 41,500, the first floor would have 20,750 sq ft of slab on grade and the second floor a similar amount of supported slab.

Excavation would be roughly 20,750 sq ft times the depth of the building below existing grade.

The first-floor concrete would equal 20,750 sq ft times the depth of the slab on grade, plus a grade wall to footer depth. Add to this the second floor slab, basing the quantity of concrete per square foot of floor on a typical bay check. Usually the concrete quantity will average .5 to .75 cu ft per sq ft of floor (or say .60 for this example). The roof slab should be slightly less than this, probably .5 cu ft per sq ft of area. An analysis follows:

	cu ft
Assume footer: 1 × 3 ft × the perimeter of the building (footer) 619 × 1 × 3 ft	1,857
Assume grade wall: 1 ft thick × 4 ft high × the perimeter (grade wall) 1 × 4 × 619 ft	2,476
Assume columns @ 18 in. sq: 45 (1.5 × 1.5 × 28 ft)	2,835
Assume column footers: (4 × 4 × 4 ft) × 21	1,344
Slab on grade: 20,750 sq ft × 5 in.	8,507
Supported slab: 20,750 sq ft × .60 cu ft per sq ft	12,450
Floor slab: 20,750 sq ft × .50 cu ft per sq ft	10,375
Total	39,844

$$\text{Total concrete} = \frac{39{,}844}{27} = 1{,}476 \text{ cu yd}$$

Thus, a check price (concrete price per square foot) for this building would be 1,476 cu yd @ $84 (average concrete price for entire building) equals $123,984 or $123,984/41,454 sq ft = $2.99.

The finished floors and ceilings can also be based on total square feet per floor, and roofing will be the same as the largest floor.

Elevators, specialties, and equipment can be priced as shown in the previous estimates. Plumbing will be the number of fixtures (with drains) times $500 to $600 for an average building. Heating and air conditioning for an average building will be roughly 300 sq ft per ton at a cost ranging from $1,000 to $1,400 per ton. Electrical usually ranges from 4 watts to 10 watts per sq ft to about $400 per kva.

The typical building shown of 41,454 sq ft would possibly have plumbing, heating and ventilating, and electrical costs as follows:

Plumbing (assume 80 fixtures @ $600)	$ 48,000
Heating and air conditioning $\left(\dfrac{41{,}454}{300} = 138 \text{ tons @ } \$1{,}200 \right)$	165,600
Electrical (assume 8 watts/sq ft) 332 kva @ $400 (8 watts × 41,454 × 0.001 watts/kw = 332)	132,800

The above analysis is only usable for a check on a detailed estimate. Such an analysis will help the estimator to visualize the project in its entirety.

The use of an estimate form is a help in preparing a workable list of quantities from the information shown on drawings.

The takeoff will be based on units of construction items comparable to those used in pricing manuals, such as concrete in cubic yards, form work in square feet, or reinforcing in pounds.

The extension of items will be simply a multiplication of units of quantities times a unit price for materials and a separate price for labor.

The total extension of material in each division will be used to add a waste or breakage factor, if necessary, and state and local taxes are added.

Adding the labor items to arrive at a total labor cost within each division will allow the estimator to add a percentage for labor fringe benefits (usually 15 to 20 percent) of labor costs. The adjusted material cost and labor costs should be added, and then general markup for profit, which will vary from 5 to 15 percent depending on the project size and complexity, should be added.

Most of the specific items within the sixteen divisions of the *Uniform Index* are self-explanatory. An exception is Division 1, General Requirements.

Included in the general requirements division are services, labor, and material which are an operating cost to the general contractor. It should be noted that most, or all, of these items cannot be charged to any one material or division. However, their costs are very real and must be borne by the general contractor.

After completion of the takeoff and extension of the unit prices, the total sum would be the amount bid at present market values. The next step in preparation of the estimate is to determine the bid date of the project and to update the estimate to the time of bidding. This factor can only be based on past performance of cost trends. The national trend has been a rise in building construction cost of about 2.75 percent per year during the past ten years.

The estimator should watch the *Engineering News-Record,* Bureau of Labor Standards, and other available indices and statistics on construction cost. Also, any available information on local bidding can be used to check on whether the national trend applies to local conditions.

The contingency allowance is generally 5 percent of the construction total, which is an allowance for unforeseen difficulties during the construction phase of the project. The total shows the project cost to the bidding date.

The architectural estimator must price all divisions. This makes his work quite different from that of the general-construction estimator.

The use of general contractors and subcontractors for estimating a project, especially during the time when working drawings are 30 to 70 percent complete, has never proved satisfactory because of the lack of available information. It is also unfair to contractors and subcontractors, since the architect does not pay for their expensive and time-consuming estimating function.

For that matter, even payment of a contractor by the architect for estimating services has proven unsatisfactory for the reasons mentioned above; also the contractor must sacrifice his estimating staff for the time used in preparation of the architect's estimate.

A full-time estimator for quantity analysis and project budgeting can be a valuable asset in an architect's office. He can provide many services in addition to estimating and cost control.

The research of unit prices for materials, trends of market values, preparation of records, and help in presentations to clients are a few functions that the estimator can perform.

The second choice would be the use of an estimating service or quantity-survey consultant, only second, in my opinion, because of the problems of communication between architectural personnel and a separate organization.

Upon completion of an estimate, the result should be closely reviewed with the project manager. The result should be a project that adheres to the budget amount set for it, providing the most building for the client's dollar. When the amount of the estimate exceeds the budget, a complete list of quantities, unit prices, and total prices of the project should be tabulated alongside those of all previous estimates. This procedure will indicate what items have been added to the building during the period between the budget preparation and the later estimate.

The tabulation form, a portion of which is shown in Fig. 14.1, contains a complete list of all of the items in the project; it is a vivid indication, to all parties concerned, of where the building dollar is going. The first tabulation is based on the preliminary drawings and specifications and accompanied with an area takeoff sheet. Note that this building used as a demonstration was designed in preliminary phase using glass-curtain wall and that between the preliminary phase and the time when working drawings were 18 percent complete, the design changed to precast concrete. Needless to say, this form will be very valuable for the budgeting of future projects, indicating, as it does, the changes that may take place after the preliminary phase.

Upon receipt of the bids, a tabulation of actual bidding on the project will show the total project picture. This tabulation will also furnish a basis for a determination of whether the increase in scope has been a result of additions by the owner, design refinements, or added size of the building due to architectural reasons.

Accompanying the breakdown of quantities and pricing should be an area sheet showing an accurate computation of what dimensions were used to arrive at the size of the building.

TABULATION 1

PROJECT NO. 1148

DEETER · RITCHEY · SIPPEL
ARCHITECTS · PLANNERS · ENGINEERS
FOUR GATEWAY CENTER
PITTSBURGH, PENNSYLVANIA 15222

GRADUATE SCHOOL OF PUBLIC HEALTH
PRELIMINARY ESTIMATE — 61,958 SF @ $28 24/SF/BLDG. — 7/6/65 — 61,958 SF

ITEM	DESCRIPTION	QUANTITY	UNITS	UNIT PRICE	PRICE SF/BLDG	PRICE TOTAL
1.	GENERAL CONDITIONS.	-----	-----	-----	1.41/SF	$ 87,500.00
2.	SITE WORK					
a	Caissons - McKinney	555	CY	90.00	0.92	60,500.00
b	Curb - Taper	250	LF	4.00	0.01	1,000.00
c	Retaining Wall & Plant Bed	100	LF	20.00	0.03	2,000.00
d	Top Soil - Planting-Bed	-----		-----	0.03	2,000.00
e	Walks	440	SY	4.50	0.03	2,000.00
f	Bituminous Paving	470	SY	4.50	0.03	2,150.00
g	Gravel Splash Pad	50	CY	18.00	0.01	900.00
h	Conc. Demolition & Cut Beam.	200	CY	20.00	0.06	4,000.00
j	Curb Straight	2,500	LF	5.00	0.20	12,500.00
k	Garage Shore	30,000	SF	0.50	0.24	9,600.00
l	Tree Protection			-0-	-0-	-0-
m	Excavation	6,000	CY	1.30	0.07	4,230.00
n	First thru 7th Floors, Alter.	2,000	SF	14.60	0.63	39,120.00
o	Granite Face Retaining Wall	-----		-----	-0-	-0-
p	Membrane - Planting Bed	-----		-----	-0-	-0-
	TOTAL SITE WORK				2.26/SF	$ 140,000.00
3. A.	CONCRETE					
a	Concrete	1,594	CY	23.00	0.59	36,662.00
b	Wall Form	6,345	SF	0.90	0.09	5,710.00
c	Beam Form	4,085	SF	1.05	0.07	4,289.00
d	Deck	96,500	SF	0.50	0.83	48,250.00
e	Reinforcing 46#/CY	65,881	LB	0.17	0.18	11,200.00
f	Mesh	109,471	SF	0.09	0.16	9,852.00
g	Finish	109,047	SF	0.24	0.46	26,171.00
h	Keyway	4,347	LF	0.23	0.02	1,000.00
j	Slag	404	TON	17.00	0.02	6,866.00
	TOTAL CONCRETE				2.42/SF	$ 150,000.00
B.	PRECAST CONCRETE					
a	Window Wall	-----		-----	-0-	-0-
b	Window Frames	-----		-----	-0-	-0-
c	Coping	-----		-----	-0-	-0-

TABULATION 2

DEETER · RITCHEY · SIPPEL
ARCHITECTS · PLANNERS · ENGINEERS
FOUR GATEWAY CENTER
PITTSBURGH, PENNSYLVANIA 15222

18% WORKING DRAWINGS — 9/22/65 — 63,665 SF @ $27 52/SF/BLDG. — 63,665 SF

DESCRIPTION	QUANTITY	UNITS	UNIT PRICE	PRICE SF/BLDG	PRICE TOTAL
GENERAL CONDITIONS	-----	-----	-----	1.58/SF	$ 100,446.00
Caissons - McKinney	693	CY	86.00	0.93	59,623.00
Curb - Taper	122	LF	4.20	0.01	514.00
Retaining Wall & Plant Bed	154	LF	36.12	0.09	5,577.00
Top Soil - Planting-Bed	78	CY	12.00	0.01	936.00
Walks	2,002	SF	0.62	0.02	1,261.00
Bituminous Paving	492	SY	4.63	0.04	2,278.00
Gravel Splash Pad	67	CY	16.50	0.02	1,116.00
Conc. Demolition & Cut Beam.	384	CY	20.00	0.13	7,688.00
Curb Straight	375	LF	4.20	0.02	1,573.00
Garage Shore	29,965	SF	0.54	0.24	16,181.00
Tree Protection			(Allow)	0.01	225.00
Excavation	2,014	CY	2.10	0.07	4,230.00
First thru 7th Floors, Alter.	2,200	SF	12.88	0.44	28,342.00
Granite Face Retaining Wall	-----		-----	-0-	-0-
Membrane - Planting Bed	-----		-----	-0-	-0-
TOTAL SITE WORK				2.03/SF	$ 129,522.00
CONCRETE					
Concrete	1,094	CY	23.00	0.39	25,162.00
Wall Form	5,242	SF	0.92	0.08	4,823.00
Beam Form	3,356	SF	1.04	0.05	3,490.00
Deck	87,473	SF	0.45	0.61	39,363.00
Reinforcing 46#/CY	63,129	LB	0.17	0.17	10,732.00
Mesh	98,514	SF	0.07	0.11	6,896.00
Finish	90,700	SF	0.21	0.30	19,047.00
Keyway	796	LF	0.23	0.01	181.00
Slag	59	TON	17.10	0.02	1,003.00
TOTAL CONCRETE				1.74/SF	$ 110,695.00
PRECAST CONCRETE					
Window Wall	184	UNITS	634.37	1.83	116,724.00
Window Frames	-----		-----	-0-	-0-
Coping	439	LF	8.01	0.06	3,516.00

FIG. 14.1 *Preliminary estimate for a graduate school of public health.*

209

This sheet is invaluable to the architect and the owner as a guide to the requirements of the building as well as in cost analysis. Each item can then be reviewed to determine what can be removed or substituted to reduce cost, if that should prove necessary. This takes a meeting with the client.

The possibility of overrating the amounts of savings for items removed at this point is a trap to be avoided. For example, the removal of vinyl tile and cove base from a project can be evaluated in dollars saved, but the addition of concrete finishing, floor hardeners, and a painted base must be added to give a true cost.

The "false savings trap," that is, the removal or substitution of items that will add cost into other divisions (such as removal of wall and roof insulation which adds tonnage in air conditioning), can easily produce additional costs rather than savings.

The substitution of items that will add to maintenance or shorten the life of a building should be carefully avoided.

If the quantity takeoff has been accurate and the unit prices realistic, the estimate should be comparable to a low-bid figure.

The practice of letting the estimate for the project remain 10 percent or more above the total allowable budget in the hope that the contractor will bid low is unrealistic. The contractor can only absorb at most 5 to 10 percent of the total cost of the structure by completely deducting his profit.

Using a system of estimating when working drawings are 30, 60, and 90 percent complete can make much useful information available.

At 30 percent of completion, the actual working drawings do not convey enough information to give an accurate picture of quantities or details. However, a review of preliminary drawings at this stage, along with the information shown on the partially completed working drawings, will show if the project is within its original scope and budget.

Upon completion of 60 percent of the working drawings, the structural portion will have been designed, and the architectural details should indicate a much more complete picture.

At this stage, the detailing of the phases of the project will indicate any changes or refinement of the original scope. And the indication of quality will be apparent. If the estimate indicates that the budget will be exceeded, the project can be trimmed before further detailing proceeds.

At 90 percent of completion of the working drawings, another estimate should be prepared to refine the previous estimate and check for any cost additions. After that, it is relatively easy to estimate the cost of a project after the drawings and specifications are complete.

In our office, we set the following schedule for project cost control estimates:

1. The budget is set at the completion of preliminary drawings and specifications.

2. At 30 percent of working-drawing completion, an estimate based on the information shown on preliminary drawings plus the amount of detail shown on working drawings to date is prepared.

3. At 60 percent of working-drawing completion, the structural system should have been designed at this point, and room finishes and exterior finish should have been designed and detailed to a point where the estimator can revise the estimate to be more realistic.

4. At 90 percent of working-drawing completion, a final estimate is prepared to be presented to the client with the working drawings.

Each of the estimates showing the additions or deductions to the project during the working-drawing phase should be presented to the client. This service will eliminate the trap in which the project grows during detailing because of additional requests of the owner plus refinements of design characteristics beyond the limitation of the budget.

Sources of cost information available to the estimator include many worthwhile pricing manuals, but the information in these books is based on average costs in the entire nation and is compiled on projects of a certain size.

Refinement of the unit prices from such sources can be made by tabulation of the cost breakdowns of bidding documents for all previous projects in the estimator's own office. In this way, the estimator can take the pulse of contractors' prices in his area, and can develop more realistic units of cost in many instances.

FIFTEEN

Norman Foster

Control during Construction

The ultimate cost of a building is part of an architect's responsibility to the owner. To design a structure, the initial bid cost of which is within the budget allowance, is not enough. The architect must also control the changes and revisions which are common to most construction contracts. Under conditions of all-around perfection there would be no change orders, no extras, and the owner would get the building and appurtenances he expected. Almost as satisfactory would be the job which had only beneficial change orders which gave a tangible change in scope equal to the dollar cost or saving.

Such ideal conditions are seldom found in construction. They would require complete understanding, coordination, and skillful cooperation, first between the owner and the architect, then between the architect and the contractor. The contracting parties have different viewpoints and aims. The owner is likely to view with suspicion extra work claims submitted by the contractor, who cannot understand why anyone would doubt such fair and reasonable requests. In the middle stands the architect, who although he is the agent of the owner, must render impartial judgment.

If cost control during construction amounted to no more than

ong as the architect and the owner know what work the contractor
t do in order to achieve the extra work, and the owner will approve
cost. However, experience has shown that architects and owners
uently express astonishment at the cost of simple extras. Sometimes
y do so with good reason—contractors can be ingenious when prepar-
change-order requests. A good architect, interested in cost control,
uld know what is fair and what is not. An extra interior door and
me may be worth $125 if authorized early in the contract. The same
or and frame could cost the contractor $500 if he has to go back
a finished wall, cut the opening, pin the lintel, patch the masonry
d plaster, rework the base board, finish the floor, and repaint the
tire wall.

Almost any change which is authorized after the trades affected have
mpleted their work will cost more than the face value of the improve-
ent. Delivery alone may be a vital factor in the cost of a simple change
rder. A late decision to change the type and color of the glass in
he window walls could bring the whole job virtually to a standstill
or weeks. One could give hundreds of examples, but it is enough to
ay that the longer a change is delayed, the more it will cost.

Changes below Ground

In lump-sum contracts, the cost of work below ground is usually subject to change should job conditions require variations from the design
or foundation grades shown on the drawings. It is also common for
the contract to be based on earth excavation, with rock excavation being
paid for as an extra cost. Such agreements in which the owner accepts
financial responsibility for actual conditions below ground should not
limit the care taken by the architect to design a structure suited to
the site conditions. Site investigations, such as taking borings and digging
test pits, should be made. All of the information relating to below-ground
conditions should be available to bidders.

Failure to include below-ground information in the contract documents or the inclusion of inaccurate information can lead to costly extra-
work claims. The contractor is entitled to rely on the adequacy of the
contract documents. The inclusion of such phrases as "the conditions
below ground as depicted are not guaranteed" does not relieve the owner
of financial responsibility for changes resulting from actual ground
conditions.

Changes in the bottom grade of concrete foundations, or in the dimensions of walls, piers, etc., should be easy to resolve. When the contract
includes a unit price for each class of concrete and excavation below
ground, the change order will be simply a matter of computation. The

authorizing beneficial change orders the responsibility would not be very
great. There are, however, many other factors that can increase the basic
cost of a construction job—errors in the drawings, misunderstandings of
scope between architect and owner, delays, a contractor who will not,
or cannot, render satisfactory performance, indecision by the architect
or the owner—the list is long.

Many of the steps towards cost control must be taken before the bidding stage. These should be touched upon before beginning a decision
of what happens during construction scope of the work.

There should be absolute understanding between the architect and
the owner about the owner's requirements, the limit of the contract,
design criteria, inclusions, exclusions, quality of material, and so forth.
Complete understanding means just that—no grey areas, no guesswork,
nothing left to chance. Much of the misunderstanding and disagreement
which follows a claim by the contractor would have been avoided if
there had been agreement on the scope of the work between the architect
and the owner. This scope of the work, in writing, should be a summary
of what the contract will cover, what is *not* included, and what are
variable items within the contract (such as work below ground).

Drawings and Specifications

The drawings and specifications should be complete, clear, and complementary. It should always be remembered that the contractor is
bound by the contract documents. He only agrees to produce the building, or buildings, and appurtenances depicted on the drawings and described in the specifications. He is not clairvoyant and cannot afford
to be altruistic. In the highly competitive field in which he operates,
the contractor makes his only contribution to the owner when he submits
a favorable bid. Beyond that, all that can be expected of him is satisfactory performance within the scope of the contract. Precise language
is the secret of good specifications. Brief, declarative sentences are the
sign of a good specification writer.

Coordination of Bid Documents

All contract documents should be coordinated to ensure coverage but
to eliminate contradictions. Especial care should be taken to coordinate
the architectural drawings and specifications with the structural, mechanical, and electrical drawings and specifications. Duplication of such items
as excavation for utilities, temporary services, concrete for the mechanical trades could mean duplication in the bid figures and thus a hidden

increase in the bid price. Errors between the architectural and engineering drawings can result in extras during construction.

General Conditions

The general conditions should be clear and complete. When standard general conditions are augmented by supplementary general conditions, care should be taken that one does not contradict the other.

Cost "Problem Items"

Cost "problem items" should be carefully specified. There are a number of such items, and they often result in major extras. The limitations of the work below ground should be spelled out. Rock excavation should be defined if it is to be extra over the contract price. Such items as dewatering, temporary heat, temporary light and power, and utility work by others should be clearly defined.

Unit Prices

Unit prices should be requested with the bid for all items which are subject to variation in quantity. The method of measurement for unit price items should be clearly defined; also the fact that all unit prices are gross prices and include overhead and profit.

Alternate Prices

Alternate prices can be valuable to the owner in helping him to decide whether or not certain variations in scope are worthwhile or can be afforded. However, a great number of complicated alternates present a real problem to the bidders. There just is not time to give each proper attention; thus the bidder errs on the side of caution—deductive alternates are bid tight (if not low), and additive items are bid high. When there is a public opening of bids, alternates should not be so extensive that they create bidding problems for the contractors. In the case of private openings, it may be to the owner's advantage to give the bidders twenty-four hours after bid time to submit alternates and unit prices.

Beneficial Changes Initiated by Owner

There should be no problem in resolving change orders which are straightforward additions to the contract and which give the owner tangible benefits requested by him. The architect should act promptly to obtain a price from the contractor and authorize the change before the work advances to a point which will prevent the required change

from being incorporated "as bid." After it has b
will get little or no credit for deducting the a
ceramic tile; in fact, he may have to pay for both
take the benefits of bulk quantity purchasing; a
feet deducted from the contract just leaves them w
have to keep in stock for years. Almost all colo
is a complete loss; slight changes in the color of
it almost impossible to incorporate surplus stock

All other things being equal, the only question
that the contractor's price is fair and reasonable. The
to, and should insist on receiving, a detailed estim
unit prices, and so forth. He should take off the
the estimator's figures; he must satisfy himself that
fair and that the extraneous cost items, such as ov
bonds, and profit, are fair and in accordance with
prices embodied in the contract should be used whe
Quantities should be net (adds less deducts) for e
stated otherwise in the contract, it is reasonable to allo
to exclude overhead and profit from purely deductive ch

Beneficial Changes Initiate

During the construction, the architect may recomm
changes in the work. Before submitting this type of re
to the owner, the architect should make sure that the
to incorporate the change without extraneous expenses
vital factor he should warn the owner and see that pro
are made. Delays in processing change orders usually ha
consequences—legitimate claims by the contractor, delay in
tion, dissatisfaction and dissension between the owner and
tor. The architect will be in a particularly uncomfortabl
delays, claims, or disagreements stem from changes which h

The checking and certification of this type of change
for all change orders: take off the quantities to check the
estimate, check unit prices, extensions, and additions, and
the change-order request is compiled in strict accordance wi
tract specifications.

Partially Beneficial Chang

Changes in interior layout, finishes, doors, and so forth whic
alterations to completed work may cost considerably more than
value of the tangible benefit which the owner seeks. This is

unit prices should be adequate but not inflated. The measurement limits of excavation should be described for each unit-price item. The unit prices for excavation should include all necessary sheeting, shoring, and dewatering (or specifically exclude these items if they are not to be included). The important thing is that the unit-price item must be described exactly and fully. If the item is simply described as "concrete in foundation walls" that is what will probably be received, regardless of what the unit price might seem to cover. Forms and reinforcing steel will be charged for separately. What may have looked like a cheap unit price could become an embarrassment, all because the architect was not explicit when he described the item.

Disagreement on quantities for changes below ground can be avoided if the contractor and the architect (or their on-site representatives) *both* keep running records of the changes. These records should be in exact agreement and should be dated and signed by both parties at least once a week.

Rock excavation can be a costly extra in a contract. If a considerable quantity of rock excavation is expected, the architect should ensure that the unit price agreed to is reasonable. It may be necessary to consider the rock unit prices when evaluating the contract bids. As in all excavation units, the payment limits for rock excavation should be clearly defined in the description of the unit-price item in the specifications. Should the owner or the architect decide that all excavation in the contract is unclassified and that there will be no extra payment for rock excavation, the drawings should include extensive below-ground investigation data. If the contractor must assume the risk, he is entitled to an excellent set of site drawings with rock elevations plotted and extensive boring information; he should be given the opportunity to make such additional investigations as he wishes during the bidding period. To withhold below-ground information from the bidders is to invite trouble. A good estimator will raise his price for earthwork to take the gamble out of his bid. Regardless of whether the cost has been adequately covered or not, the contractor is going to make a claim against the owner if the conditions below ground are radically worse than the contract documents depicted. And if it is revealed that vital information, known to the architect or owner, was withheld from the bidders, the contractor will be even more unhappy, and rightly so. In such a case, deterioration of the relationship between the contracting parties is inevitable.

In his handling of below-ground conditions then, the cost-conscious architect can best serve the owner by:

1. Carefully studying the actual below-ground conditions and designing the foundations to suit those factors

2. Incorporating into the contract fair unit prices for extra work below ground

3. Ensuring that proper records are kept of the actual foundations as installed

4. Checking the accuracy of the contractor's change-order requests, for both quantities and unit prices

5. Ensuring that the bidders have access to all the data they require to evaluate the cost of work below ground

Changes due to Architect's Errors or Omissions

A change order which is needed to correct an error by the architect may still give the owner some degree of value for his money. Although it may be embarrassing for an architect to admit that he has made a mistake, the owner should realize that if the change adds something of benefit to him, he should pay for it. Nevertheless, a conscientious architect will do everything in his power to ensure that the job, as designed and specified, is exactly what the owner has requested. Careful coordination with structural, mechanical engineers, and other consultants will go a long way toward preventing this type of change order. However, we all make mistakes—owners, contractors, and architects. So long as the architect is satisfied that the amount of the change-order request is fair, he should approve it and submit it to the owner.

Changes to Satisfy Local Authorities

In an attempt to circumvent claims by the contractor, or to control the cost of the work, some architects use a general condition clause which, at its face value, makes the contractor responsible for complying with all state and local ordinances, laws, and building codes. Such a clause usually goes on to say that no extra payment will be permitted for claims arising from work required to meet such codes. This, of course, is blatantly unfair and, legally, is difficult to uphold. Legal factors apart, every architect should design structures which comply with the applicable building codes. This is one of his basic responsibilities. The basic responsibility of the contractor is to construct the project in strict accordance with the drawings and specifications. If there is any doubt of compliance, or if the design incorporates ideas or material not covered by the codes, the questionable factors should be cleared with the local authorities during design stage. Many items in local building codes are vague or seem to cover only broad and general factors. Clarifications by building authorities, or their acceptance of new designs not covered by existing codes, should be written decisions. It is neither prudent nor safe to accept only the verbal approval of a public official in this type of finding. Policy changes, staff changes, even honest disagreements on "who said exactly what" can have unhappy consequences.

Failure to meet the local building codes or to obtain written agreement from the local authorities for special design factors can have extremely expensive repercussions. Many costly cases come to mind: an entire storm-drainage system which had to be replaced because the codes did not allow the type of pipe specified; a verbal decision on the meaning of "fireproofed doors and millwork," which was later denied; twenty flights of concrete stairs with 3 in. less headroom than the code allowed; dozens of stairwell walls which had to be plastered on both sides to meet the code because the architect thought 6-in. concrete block was acceptable.

If, during construction, some doubt should arise over compliance with local codes, the architect should act promptly. First, he should instruct the contractor to suspend work on the phase of the job which is questioned. Next, he should meet with the local building department and press for an immediate decision. The contractor should be invited to this conference if he can help in any way. Should the architect receive only a verbal decision, he should write to the local authority (copy to the contractors) confirming the fact that he is proceeding with the work in accordance with their verbal instructions. This letter must be explicit and complete; it is less satisfactory than written authority, but better than merely accepting the verbal decision.

Extra Costs of No Benefit to Owner

Change orders which give the owner no value for his money are most unsatisfactory to everyone concerned and are usually the result of carelessness and lack of foresight by someone. The most common of such extraneous costs, for which the architect is responsible, are those caused by errors in the drawings or from inadequate specifications. Poor coordination of the structural, mechanical, and architectural drawings often cause trouble on the job, and frequently result in extra costs which benefit no one. Errors in dimensions, inadequate structural design, ductwork oversized for the available space, openings placed without regard to masonry coursing, catch basins in the wrong places—these are examples of improper design which eventually cost the owner extra money. A good contractor will do all that can reasonably be expected of him to adjust things, correct errors, and help solve minor problems. Contractors cannot be expected, at their own expense, to pull the job out of a mess caused by the architect.

Cost control during construction starts with a good set of drawings and clear, complete specifications. Contractors can afford to, and will, tighten their bids when they have confidence in the architect. The bidding documents tell the contractor a great deal about the architect. When the extent and limits of the contract are clear cut, the contractors will react favorably. Every contractor wants a straightforward set of contract documents. He wants a job which gives him a fair chance. He wants to "get in and get out." Delays awaiting changes in design, or caused by errors in the documents, cost money. Few change orders are beneficial to the contractor. Most of them are a nuisance and cost more to process than they are worth. An extra of $1,000 probably gives the contractor only about $100 profit margin, but will cost him hours of estimating and clerical work—*and will hold up the job.*

When an architect finds that he has trouble getting contractors to bid his jobs, he may be sure that there is something wrong with either his contract documents or his attitude towards contractors, or both. Maximum effort by the architect in both areas will go far towards ensuring minimum cost to his client.

Sometimes it becomes necessary or prudent to authorize a change order simply to keep the job moving. Delay in the receipt of specified materials can hold up the entire job. Such delays may not be the fault of anyone directly responsible for the project. It could be a strike in a factory, a breakdown in transportation systems, a shortage of raw materials, or any of a dozen factors beyond the control of contractor or architect.

Having satisfied himself that the project faces a delay which the owner cannot afford, the architect should promptly examine the available alternatives. It may be possible to substitute stock items, or authorize another make or model. The extent to which the architect and the owner go in relaxing the specifications should depend on the importance of the time that would be saved in completing the project. The one item or material under question may not be the key to the problem. There is no advantage in changing one item only to find that some other item has the whole job stymied anyway. Thus, before making the change, the architect should be reasonably sure that nothing else is going to slow down the job. Are all of the shop drawings coming along and being processed with ample time left for fabrication and delivery? Is the contractor dragging out the job anyway? Is the owner taking care of the purchase of furniture and so forth? Will the owner be ready to occupy the building on the anticipated completion date? Is the change going to cost more than the time saving is worth?

Many change orders of this nature can be circumvented before they occur. The architect can make sure that he is using current information when he specifies proprietary items. He can remind the contractor when shop drawings and material samples are vital and are due to be submitted. He can process shop drawings expeditiously. He can insist that the contractor give him an equipment report every month, showing the order number, date of order, and promised delivery dates for all major items of equipment and material vital to job progress.

Change Orders Requested by Contractor

Change-order requests initiated by the contractor are generally with respect to work which the contractor claims to be over and beyond the contract requirements. They may be for work which the contractor claims was necessary through no fault of his, or they may be for work ordered by the architect or his representative. When the contractor initiates a request for a change order, it usually means that the architect did not recognize a bona fide extra in the first instance. Sometimes an architect will, without realizing the consequences, order certain work or procedures. Every time the architect, or his representative, renders a decision, he should be certain of his ground. If the work or procedure is within the contract requirements, he must be sure that the contractor knows this and understands the authority or basis on which the decision rests. If the work is not within the contract requirements, the architect should proceed in accordance with the extra-work paragraph of the specifications.

If there is an honest difference of opinion between the architect and the contractor, the architect may exercise whatever power is vested in him by the contract documents. If the contract allows it, the contractor may elect to carry out the work while reserving his rights to arbitration or legal action. In most cases, it should be possible for an architect and a contractor to reach an agreement on extra-work claims. It requires good faith and mutual trust and may even call for a measure of compromise, but a little give and take is much better than a costly legal action.

Claims Arising from Contractor's Rights

The contractor has certain rights. Some are embodied in the written contract; some have been established by precedent-setting court decision. These rights give rise to thousands of claims every year; in fact, one or more crop up on almost every project. The architect should know what these rights are and should guard against impinging upon them. Whether covered by the contract or not, there are some basic and common rights for which many contractors have fought successful legal actions. Some of these are described in the following:

1. *Right to Access to the Site of the Work* Limited only by restrictions or terms specifically covered by the contract documents, the contractor has a right to unimpeded access to the site. If, through the actions or negligence of the owner, or the owner's representative, the contractor is denied free access to the site, he may have a claim against the owner. This may happen for such reasons as right of way not obtained, land purchase not completed, demolition not completed, work by other contractors insufficiently advanced. The architect should do everything within his power to prevent such situations. When the contractor is unable to get his job started, relations become strained, and the project is off to a bad start. In such cases, there are contractors who are experts at preparing the maximum claim their ingenuity can devise.

2. *Failure to Obtain Building Permit* This could take one of two forms; either the owner failed to obtain the building permit, or having specified that the contractor is to obtain it, the authorities refused to grant the contractor a permit on the grounds that the project does not comply with their regulations. In either case, since the delay is not his fault, the contractor may claim damages. The architect can guard against this type of claim by ensuring that his drawings comply with the local codes and that a permit will be granted.

Time will be saved if the owner obtains the building permit before the contractor is ready to start work, although, of course, this is not always possible. In some communities, the contractor is required to apply for the building permit. Regardless of how, or by whom, there is no excuse for circumstances which leave the contractor high and dry for weeks while the architect submits design criteria to the local building department or argues about the permit.

3. *Suspension of Work by the Owner* When all work is stopped by the owner, the contractor usually has a right to a damages claim. This may be no problem if the suspension is temporary, but can become a problem if the stoppage lasts for several weeks. If the job is to be abandoned entirely, the architect may become involved in a complex evaluation of the work completed and in an assessment of the settlement due to the contractor. In these cases, it may be advisable to use the services of a professional construction estimator to make an independent survey. Regardless of the nature of a pending suspension of work, the architect should forewarn the owner of possible action by the contractor. It may be prudent to suggest that the owner obtain legal advice, since breach of contract might be involved.

4. *Failure to Make Payments* Most construction contracts clearly define the way in which the contractor will receive payment. Failure of the owner to make a payment when it becomes due can constitute cause for a claim by the contractor. The architect can do his part towards

preventing such a situation by acting promptly to agree upon the amount of the requisition with the contractor and by forwarding the certified request for payment to the owner.

Receipt of his payments promptly is very important to the contractor. Prompt payment is also the one most vital factor which is guaranteed to consolidate contractor-owner relations. Conversely, delays in making payments to the contractor will definitely cause a deterioration in relations. When the architect finds it necessary to cut the contractor's requisition, he should explain his reasons to the contractor. This is more than a matter of courtesy; the contractor is entitled to know how his requisition has been changed, and why.

5. *Failure of Architect to Render Decisions* Financial claims by the contractor arising from time delays allegedly caused by the architect are not common, but they do occur. At their worst, such claims can be costly to the architect; at the least, they do his reputation no good. As a cost-control factor, such claims may successfully support extension of time claims and thus offset liquidated damage claims against the contractor. Either way, such claims may cost the owner money, and the possibility of the architect becoming personally involved must not be discounted. These types of claims can easily be avoided by not delaying decisions. Check and return shop drawings promptly; render all opinions and decisions expeditiously. If there are complications which delay things, the architect should keep the contractor informed and help him to keep the job moving.

6. *Delays Caused by "Owner-awarded" Contracts* The award of separate contracts by the owner (i.e., contracts not controlled by the general contractor) imposes upon the owner and the architect additional responsibilities. If the contractor's work is held up because the separate contracts have not been awarded or because of unsatisfactory progress by the separate contractors, the general contractor may have just cause for a claim against the owner. Basically, no one has the right to impede the contractor in the execution of his contract. It is therefore important that the architect do all he can towards seeing that this does not happen.

The case for separate contracts is debatable, to say the least. If there are good reasons for the award of separate contracts, the overall job progress may best be served by giving the general contractor control of the separate contracts. This may cost the owner an agreed fixed fee or a percentage of the contract amounts. A general contractor is likely to ask for from 1 to 5 percent for administering and coordinating separate contracts. An efficient general contractor will earn the extra fee. When this is done, there can be no question of the general contractor claiming damages because the owner-managed contracts are impeding his progress.

Third-party Claims against the Owner

Efficient cost control should include protection of the owner from situations which could leave him open to third-party claims against him. Such claims could arise from infringement upon adjoining property, or might involve a third-party claim in which the owner is enjoined with the contractor.

To take the second case first, the owner will be protected against being drawn into claims against the contractor if the public liability insurance section of the general conditions requires that the contractor take out contractual liability, including "hold harmless," insurance. The actual wording in the general conditions need only require that the contractor "indemnify the owner against all suits and actions arising out of the contract and hold the owner harmless from all claims due to the contractor's operations within the contract." The question of the owner's involvement in third-party claims should be even more seriously considered when, as is becoming quite common, an owner takes over all the insurance for his project.

Damage to adjoining property may take any of several forms. Sometimes the architect will show a wall right on the property line without having given any consideration to the rights of the adjoining property owners. Many jobs have become bogged down in lawsuits because the excavations or work on foundation walls encroached on adjoining land. It just is not possible to build right up to the property line without affecting the other owner's land to some degree. Even if sheet piling is driven, it should be a few inches inside one's own boundary line if there is to be due regard for the other landowner.

Every aspect must be explored before building anything right up to the property line. If approached in advance, most landowners are amenable, and if it is absolutely necessary to build right up to their line, they will usually make some satisfactory arrangements.

There are other ways in which an owner can become involved in claims by adjoining property owners, for example, failure to provide right of way, allowing debris to spill over onto another person's land, blocking the access to adjoining property, disregard of zoning laws or codes. If the architect should fail to do everything within his power to safeguard the owner against infringement of the rights of other property owners, he is certain to expose the owner to extra costs.

Failure of Contractor to Complete Contract

When the contractor fails to complete the contract, the owner faces what is probably the most costly loss that can arise out of a construction contract. Even if the contractor has been bonded, the time loss and the administrative work just to get the job moving again cost money. Not even a 100 percent performance and payment bond will give the owner complete financial protection. If a surety company can show that the contractor has been overpaid, or that the owner had failed to obtain proof of "payment of obligations" as required by the contract, the surety company will probably have a case against the owner.

There is an abundance of legal precedent in support of the right of the surety company to reasonable protection against losses which are caused by the owner's negligence. If the job has not been bonded, the owner usually winds up paying heavily. Protecting the owner against contractor failure is part of the architect's job and is a cost-control matter. With rare exceptions, a contractor does not go bankrupt because of his latest job; generally such a condition has been building up for months, or even years. If a contractor is solvent when he starts a job and goes bankrupt because of factors on that job, his price was too low, or he badly mishandled the job.

The precautions are simple to implement, but the right decision is not so easy. It is not sufficient to accept a contractor at face value. Some of the largest and most respected contractors in the country have gone bankrupt. Every week, somewhere in the U.S., a contractor with a good reputation in his community goes bankrupt, to the surprise of his friends, neighbors, and clients. In 1965, over 1,000 general contractors failed, leaving liabilities that averaged almost $200,000 per contractor. Thus, it is proper and prudent to be absolutely sure that the contractor has the financial ability, the technical skill, and the integrity to perform the contract.

Investigation of a proposed contractor should start by obtaining his current financial statement. It should be noted that the moment the architect begins asking for information, some contractors will try to brush him off. A good contractor, who is solvent, and who wants the job, will cooperate with the architect. The only financial statement worth anything is one prepared by a certified public accountant. When a CPA signs the statement, he stakes his professional reputation that to the best of his knowledge and belief, the information is accurate and complete. This does not guarantee the accuracy of the financial statement, but only the most dishonest contractors would juggle their books to hide debts from a CPA.

Not all architects are qualified to assess a financial statement, but every architect knows someone who can. He may be the owner's accountant, the architect's accountant, or a banker. There are a few important things to look for. What is the net worth? What is the earned surplus? How much of the net worth is in liquid assets? How much of the net worth is tied up in fixed assets such as buildings and fixtures?

Having established the contractor's financial status, the architect should check some other important factors. By checking the contractor's previous work, and the owners and architects he has worked with, the architect may satisfy himself on the quality of the work done by the contractor, his ability to finish his jobs on time, and his general reputation. A contractor may be somewhat shaky financially, yet have such a well-earned reputation for integrity and performance that he is a good risk. Another contractor may be financially strong but have a history of poor performance, unethical practice, and trouble-strewn jobs.

Of course, one of the most important factors in deciding upon a contractor is the amount of his bid and its relationship to the other bids. Even in public construction, discretionary power is vested in the awarding authorities. The commonly used term "lowest responsible bidder" must not be assumed to mean "the lowest bidder." The awarding authority may request the assistance of the architect in investigating the apparent low bidder. Providing that the awarding authorities act in good faith, without malice, dishonesty, or collusion, their decision regarding what is the lowest *responsible* bid will stand up against a legal test.

Therefore, public or private bids can be examined in, basically, the same way. A very low bid should always be suspected. If this bid is that of a reputable contractor who is financially sound, and who can be expected to perform even if his bid is too tight, there is no problem. If, however, the bid comes from another sort of contractors, and especially if the job is larger than he normally tackles, he should be investigated thoroughly; he might be desperate for a "fast buck." Often, the tabulation of all bids received serves as a warning. If a contractor, whose ability is doubtful, is very low and if he is followed by two or three good bidders grouped closely together, there is probably something wrong with the low bid.

Having decided on the contractor, in the case of private work, it may be necessary to decide whether to bond him or not. In passing, it should be noted that the ability to obtain a bond does not testify to the contractor's strength or integrity. Bonding companies can be wrong, a fact witnessed by the losses some of them have incurred. If a thorough investigation has satisfied the owner and the architect that they have the right contractor, but his financial status is a little shaky, it probably would be wise to bond him. The cost of the bond may be considerably less than the extra cost of going to the next-lowest acceptable bidder.

With the award of the contract, the architect's responsibility for cost control includes *disbursement* of the owner's money. This often means holding down a contractor who is determined to get his hands on as much money as possible as soon as possible. The first essential is to obtain from the contractor a "Contract Breakdown for Payment Purposes." Contractors have most of the human failings, including that of seeking a personal advantage. They will unbalance their breakdowns to draw as much from the job as possible in the first few payments. They will claim (and not without an element of truth) that with a 10 or 15 percent retention clause, plus the delay in receiving payments, they can never get ahead of the owner. It is true that there is a leveling-off point after which the contractor will not be ahead, but this may not be reached until somewhere beyond the halfway mark in the construction. It comes when most of the balance of work is to be done by the subtrades, and the accumulated retainage is a substantial amount. In the early stages, the contractor could get well ahead of the owner if he grossly inflated the value of such items as excavations, foundations, and structural concrete or steel. It is up to the architect to see that the breakdown is fair and reasonable.

Requisitions for periodic payments should be checked very carefully. Some architects like to have the total quantities for the major items with the initial breakdown, and the quantities completed with each request for payment. Thus, for example, with a total of 1,550 cu yd of foundation concrete for a total cost of $83,700 on the initial breakdown, it can be seen that this work averages $54 per cu yd. Each requisition will give the yardage completed, and the value of foundation concrete in place is computed at $54 per cu yd. Whatever method is used, the architect should protect the owner against loss due to overpayment. If the job is going well, a wise architect will not begrudge the contractor every penny to which he is entitled and will, if necessary, press the owner to make the payments promptly. This is the best inducement for the contractor to keep up the good work.

If the contractor is in financial difficulties, there will be obvious danger signals. The job will drag; to keep the payroll down, he will cut the crew; subcontractors will probably be checking with the architect or the owner to see what happened to their previous month's requisitions; liens will be filed by suppliers or subcontractors; the contractor will almost beg for payment of the current requisition. If, in the face of this kind of evidence, the architect does not seek an early showdown with the contractor, he is failing his responsibility to the owner.

Architects, owners, and bonding companies sometimes show an amazing degree of trust in contractors. A factual case will illustrate this. One job was about $300,000; the low bidder was $12,000 below the second bidder. Within the industry, it was well known that the low bidder was in a very shaky position. He was awarded the job and went bankrupt, and the architect turned to the second bidder to finish the job. It was then revealed that no one had ever thought of asking the first contractor for a financial statement. "I'll never do that again," said the architect—then proceeded to negotiate with the new contractor and awarded him the job, *without asking him for a financial statement.* Nor did the owners question the integrity or status of their new contractor.

Illegal Contracts

When a contract is declared to be illegal, and is voided by the courts, the owner, the contractor, and the architect all stand to lose. The courts have tended to show no sympathy towards any party who faces heavy losses in such a case; parties who arrange or enter into contractual agreements are presumed to know the law. Although not a party to the contract, the architect usually recommends the contractor or advises the owner in some degree. Therefore, an architect should know the law or obtain good counsel.

Public contracts, in particular, must comply strictly with the applicable laws. In states which have complex bidding laws, it can require a legal mind just to determine which is the lowest bid. If there is the slightest doubt surrounding the legality of a proposed contract award, the architect should not hesitate to bring in lawyers to settle the point.

"Wrap-up" Insurance by Owner

Many owners have, in recent years, bought blanket insurance as a cost-reduction factor on their construction projects. The owner hopes, and expects, that the blanket coverage will cost him less than the combined cost of the insurance bought by each of the contractors on the job. There is no doubt that on a cost-plus job, on which all of the trades are working "time and material," the owner can probably save by insuring the job himself. But in all other contracts, the owner is going to pay for some of the insurance twice.

Most general contractors will understand what is meant by the bidding condition that the price is to exclude the cost of workmen's compensation, public liability and property-damages insurance. Many subbidders simply ignore this kind of condition; many of them don't even know what their insurance costs them; some of them believe that they are legally obligated to insure their men, no matter what anyone says. What is more, their insurance agents often encourage such thinking. It is also true that if a contractor, or subcontractor, has a substantial labor force on a job, for which he does not carry the insurance, he may lose experience credits or rate benefits. Because of these factors, the amount deducted by contractors from the bids when the owner carries the insurance will invariably be less than the real value of the applicable insurance. Many subs will price the job with insurance included, then deduct a nominal amount.

Value Engineering

Value engineering is the name given to a cost-saving idea which is widely used by the Bureau of Yards and Docks. Also used by many owners, both public and private, value engineering is a new name and a new set of rules for an old idea. The idea is to give the owner the benefit of the contractor's practical knowledge when he comes up with changes that save money without adversely affecting either the scope or quality of the project. As an incentive, the contractor receives a fair share of the savings, usually 50 percent.

Confronted with value-engineering suggestions, some architects have shown themselves to be extremely sensitive to what they consider to be implied criticism of their designs or documents. Owners have been known to view their architects with suspicion when a contractor came up with a sound idea which saved a substantial amount of money. In these respective reactions, both owners and architects are very short-sighted. None of us knows it all. Savings suggested by the contractor may be the accumulated ideas of mechanical subs, electrical subs, job superintendent, and trained estimators. Taking advantage of their knowledge of conditions on the job, or their flair for comparative costs as applied to the project, these construction men are uniquely capable of knowing where savings are possible.

There are some aspects of value engineering that are important to the architect and which he should impress upon the owner. It should be understood that the architect will examine and render an opinion on all items which involve design factors. It is also usually agreed that his fees will not be reduced as a result of value-engineering deductions. Thus assured, the architect should be able to participate in value engineering with enthusiasm, and with the interest of his client in mind.

The architect should check the accuracy of the quantities and the unit prices used in the contractor's suggested value-engineering changes. It must *not* be presumed that because he receives a large share of the savings, the contractor will take pains to show the maximum credit amount. For example, if the contractor's private computations show that he anticipates a saving of $2,000, submitted strictly as computed, a 50 percent participation would give him $1,000. However, if he can juggle the quantities and unit prices to submit a saving of $1,800, he stands to make $900 plus the $200 he shaved off, or $1,100 in all. Not all contractors are that devious, but the architect should do everything within his power to ensure that the owner receives the proper credit.

Cost-plus-fee Contracts

The award of a construction contract on a cost-plus-fee basis will usually cost the owner more money than he would pay if the job were put out to competitive bidders. The cost-plus contract has certain advantages: the contractor can be handpicked; the contractor can be drawn into a team along with the owner and the architect to develop an economic project; the job can be started without waiting for complete drawings and specifications, with every possibility that the completion date will be advanced as a result. These benefits may more than offset the probable increase in initial cost, particularly if early occupation of the building has a monetary significance.

The choice of the contractor is not a matter about which anyone can be dogmatic. Much depends upon what the owner considers to be most important to him. Does he want a cheap job? A good job? A fast job? A trouble-free job? A mixture of all four? Called upon to advise the owner or to supervise the contract, the architect must evaluate certain factors. Does the contractor run an efficient job? Does he operate economically? Does he take pride in doing a good job? Does he have a top-quality supervisory and engineering staff? Is the job office overstaffed? Is the job overloaded with dormant equipment? Is the contractor using his purchasing powers for the maximum benefit to the owner? Is the job progress satisfactory?

On cost-plus jobs, the amount of the fee is not nearly as important as the choice of the contractor. The right contractor may well earn a fee of 4 or 5 percent, while another contractor could be expensive at a 2 percent fee. The most economical fee-type contract for an owner is the "Guaranteed Maximum Contract" with an incentive clause. The drawings and specifications must be reasonably complete, if the contractor is to give the owner a guaranteed-maximum cost plus a fixed fee. In this case, the owner's costs cannot exceed the guaranteed maximum plus the fee as adjusted by approved change orders. The incentive clause gives the contractor part of the savings should the final cost be less than the guaranteed maximum. The contractor's participation in the savings is sometimes 50 percent but is seldom less than 25 percent. Change orders must be handled, separately, at an agreed fee. With a good contractor—one who has worked with the architect to effect all acceptable economies before the contract is made—this is a very satisfactory type of contract to the owner.

Project Representative (Clerk of the Works)

The job project representative, or clerk of the works, is often under the jurisdiction of the architect. This job representative can be of great help, but quite often he is a hindrance to the whole project. Cost control will suffer if his work is unsatisfactory. Too many of these people lack depth of construction knowledge and the administrative ability demanded of them if they are to do their job properly. The fact is that owners or architects don't often pay the amount of money that attracts good men. On most jobs, the contractor's superintendent will get at least 50 percent more pay than the clerk of the works—and any ordinary tradesman who knows only his own craft can earn more.

A really good project representative is worth as much to the owner and architect as a good superintendent is to the contractor. He will safeguard the owner's interests, see that the contractor conforms to the contract, ensure that the workmanship is the best possible within the scope of the contract. He will also be an extra pair of eyes, working with the superintendent to their mutual benefit. There is no more miserable individual to work with than the project representative who deliberately waits until a particular item of work is finished, then says "tear it out, it's not right . . ." He should bring up his objections or ideas immediately, as they occur to him. He should aid in the progress of the project. Inept project representatives usually fit one of two categories; either they are easy-going and stay out of the way, or they spend all their time complaining about petty things.

An architect who is interested in cost control should not tolerate an inept project representative, nor should he expect to get a good one cheaply. If the project cannot afford a good man, save the money—it would be better not to put anyone on the job.

Time Schedules

The completion date is an important item in most construction contracts. Occupancy of his new building is vital to an owner. Whether a matter of earning power, vacating rented property, selling property to be vacated, an urgently needed school or hospital—every new building is badly needed, or the owner would not be investing in it. Satisfactory progress towards completion of the project is therefore an important factor in cost control. The architect and the owner are sometimes more responsible for job delays than they realize. A good contractor knows that time is money and hates to waste it. A poor contractor, whose jobs drag endlessly, probably shouldn't have been given the contract.

It is normal to request that the contractor submit a time schedule within a few days of being awarded a contract. It is important to impress upon the contractor that his time schedule must be realistic. A responsible contractor realizes that, having agreed to do a certain job by a fixed date, it is up to him to plan the work to meet that completion date. His time schedule may be anything from a simple bar chart to a detailed critical-path schedule.

Critical-path scheduling is generally believed to be a real breakthrough in time scheduling. Prepared by the contractor, CPM does make him think through the job step by step, and should help him to pinpoint probable bottlenecks. However, there are a lot of "CPM specialists" who know little or nothing about construction and therefore have to rely on production factors given to them by the contractor. A really good contractor knows the critical items with—or without—a CPM chart. This is not meant as a criticism of critical path, but only as a warning that it can be no better than the judgment of the people who establish the productivity figures.

Regardless of the type of time schedule used, and regardless of what a critical path shows, there are certain operations on a building project that are *always* critical. They are the deliveries or trades which can always tie up the job: reinforcing steel for foundations; the structural frame (whether steel or concrete); the exterior skin of the building; interior partitions; door bucks; wet-finish trades, such as plastering terrazzo, and ceramic tile; any equipment or specialty items that need a very long lead time for delivery.

Time schedules may be basically the contractor's problem, but the architect can also aid or impede completion of the project. One thing is certain; a day lost is gone, and there is no such thing as making it up. If the job stands still awaiting a decision by the architect or owner, time will be lost. Extensive change orders will delay completion of any project. A seemingly innocuous change in a pump can delay all of the heating work. A delay in awarding the finish hardware (when carried as an allowance) will delay fabrication of the metal door bucks, and that could slow the whole job down.

The important point is that if the architect or owner slows down the contractor, completion of the job will be delayed. This has nothing to do with whether or not the contractor is pushing the job to the best of his ability. An efficient architect will aid in the progress of the project, while a less efficient architect combined with a slack contractor will hinder it, and the owner will be the greatest sufferer.

Basic Guide to Cost Control during Construction

1. The scope of the contract between the owner and the architect should be clear, precise, and in writing.

2. Drawings and specifications should be complete, clear, and precise.

3. Important unit prices should be incorporated into the contract.

4. The financial status and responsibility of proposed contractor should be investigated.

5. Contract breakdown for payment should not be unbalanced.

6. Overpaying the contractor should be guarded against.

7. Time schedules and progress should be satisfactory.

8. *All* decisions should be rendered promptly.

9. The laws relating to contractual relationships should be understood and observed.

10. The rights of *both* owner and contractor should be understood and observed.

11. All quantities and prices in contractor's change estimates should be carefully checked.

12. Only a first-class construction man should be accepted as project representative (clerk of the works).

13. It takes prompt action to save a job that begins to "go sour."

Index

as long as the architect and the owner know what work the contractor must do in order to achieve the extra work, and the owner will approve the cost. However, experience has shown that architects and owners frequently express astonishment at the cost of simple extras. Sometimes they do so with good reason—contractors can be ingenious when preparing change-order requests. A good architect, interested in cost control, should know what is fair and what is not. An extra interior door and frame may be worth $125 if authorized early in the contract. The same door and frame could cost the contractor $500 if he has to go back to a finished wall, cut the opening, pin the lintel, patch the masonry and plaster, rework the base board, finish the floor, and repaint the entire wall.

Almost any change which is authorized after the trades affected have completed their work will cost more than the face value of the improvement. Delivery alone may be a vital factor in the cost of a simple change order. A late decision to change the type and color of the glass in the window walls could bring the whole job virtually to a standstill for weeks. One could give hundreds of examples, but it is enough to say that the longer a change is delayed, the more it will cost.

Changes below Ground

In lump-sum contracts, the cost of work below ground is usually subject to change should job conditions require variations from the design or foundation grades shown on the drawings. It is also common for the contract to be based on earth excavation, with rock excavation being paid for as an extra cost. Such agreements in which the owner accepts financial responsibility for actual conditions below ground should not limit the care taken by the architect to design a structure suited to the site conditions. Site investigations, such as taking borings and digging test pits, should be made. All of the information relating to below-ground conditions should be available to bidders.

Failure to include below-ground information in the contract documents or the inclusion of inaccurate information can lead to costly extra-work claims. The contractor is entitled to rely on the adequacy of the contract documents. The inclusion of such phrases as "the conditions below ground as depicted are not guaranteed" does not relieve the owner of financial responsibility for changes resulting from actual ground conditions.

Changes in the bottom grade of concrete foundations, or in the dimensions of walls, piers, etc., should be easy to resolve. When the contract includes a unit price for each class of concrete and excavation below ground, the change order will be simply a matter of computation. The from being incorporated "as bid." After it has been ordered, the owner will get little or no credit for deducting the asphalt tile and adding ceramic tile; in fact, he may have to pay for both materials. Contractors take the benefits of bulk quantity purchasing; a few hundred square feet deducted from the contract just leaves them with material they may have to keep in stock for years. Almost all colored material not used is a complete loss; slight changes in the color of different runs makes it almost impossible to incorporate surplus stock into future jobs.

All other things being equal, the only question is that of ensuring that the contractor's price is fair and reasonable. The architect is entitled to, and should insist on receiving, a detailed estimate with quantities, unit prices, and so forth. He should take off the quantities to check the estimator's figures; he must satisfy himself that the unit prices are fair and that the extraneous cost items, such as overhead, insurance, bonds, and profit, are fair and in accordance with the contract. Unit prices embodied in the contract should be used wherever they apply. Quantities should be net (adds less deducts) for each item. Unless stated otherwise in the contract, it is reasonable to allow the contractor to exclude overhead and profit from purely deductive change orders.

Beneficial Changes Initiated by Architect

During the construction, the architect may recommend beneficial changes in the work. Before submitting this type of recommendation to the owner, the architect should make sure that there is still time to incorporate the change without extraneous expenses. If time is a vital factor he should warn the owner and see that prompt decisions are made. Delays in processing change orders usually have unpleasant consequences—legitimate claims by the contractor, delay in final completion, dissatisfaction and dissension between the owner and the contractor. The architect will be in a particularly uncomfortable position if delays, claims, or disagreements stem from changes which he originated.

The checking and certification of this type of change is the same for all change orders: take off the quantities to check the contractor's estimate, check unit prices, extensions, and additions, and ensure that the change-order request is compiled in strict accordance with the contract specifications.

Partially Beneficial Change Orders

Changes in interior layout, finishes, doors, and so forth which involve alterations to completed work may cost considerably more than the face value of the tangible benefit which the owner seeks. This is all right increase in the bid price. Errors between the architectural and engineering drawings can result in extras during construction.

General Conditions

The general conditions should be clear and complete. When standard general conditions are augmented by supplementary general conditions, care should be taken that one does not contradict the other.

Cost "Problem Items"

Cost "problem items" should be carefully specified. There are a number of such items, and they often result in major extras. The limitations of the work below ground should be spelled out. Rock excavation should be defined if it is to be extra over the contract price. Such items as dewatering, temporary heat, temporary light and power, and utility work by others should be clearly defined.

Unit Prices

Unit prices should be requested with the bid for all items which are subject to variation in quantity. The method of measurement for unit price items should be clearly defined; also the fact that all unit prices are gross prices and include overhead and profit.

Alternate Prices

Alternate prices can be valuable to the owner in helping him to decide whether or not certain variations in scope are worthwhile or can be afforded. However, a great number of complicated alternates present a real problem to the bidders. There just is not time to give each proper attention; thus the bidder errs on the side of caution—deductive alternates are bid tight (if not low), and additive items are bid high. When there is a public opening of bids, alternates should not be so extensive that they create bidding problems for the contractors. In the case of private openings, it may be to the owner's advantage to give the bidders twenty-four hours after bid time to submit alternates and unit prices.

Beneficial Changes Initiated by Owner

There should be no problem in resolving change orders which are straightforward additions to the contract and which give the owner tangible benefits requested by him. The architect should act promptly to obtain a price from the contractor and authorize the change before the work advances to a point which will prevent the required change authorizing beneficial change orders the responsibility would not be very great. There are, however, many other factors that can increase the basic cost of a construction job—errors in the drawings, misunderstandings of scope between architect and owner, delays, a contractor who will not, or cannot, render satisfactory performance, indecision by the architect or the owner—the list is long.

Many of the steps towards cost control must be taken before the bidding stage. These should be touched upon before beginning a decision of what happens during construction scope of the work.

There should be absolute understanding between the architect and the owner about the owner's requirements, the limit of the contract, design criteria, inclusions, exclusions, quality of material, and so forth. Complete understanding means just that—no grey areas, no guesswork, nothing left to chance. Much of the misunderstanding and disagreement which follows a claim by the contractor would have been avoided if there had been agreement on the scope of the work between the architect and the owner. This scope of the work, in writing, should be a summary of what the contract will cover, what is *not* included, and what are variable items within the contract (such as work below ground).

Drawings and Specifications

The drawings and specifications should be complete, clear, and complementary. It should always be remembered that the contractor is bound by the contract documents. He only agrees to produce the building, or buildings, and appurtenances depicted on the drawings and described in the specifications. He is not clairvoyant and cannot afford to be altruistic. In the highly competitive field in which he operates, the contractor makes his only contribution to the owner when he submits a favorable bid. Beyond that, all that can be expected of him is satisfactory performance within the scope of the contract. Precise language is the secret of good specifications. Brief, declarative sentences are the sign of a good specification writer.

Coordination of Bid Documents

All contract documents should be coordinated to ensure coverage but to eliminate contradictions. Especial care should be taken to coordinate the architectural drawings and specifications with the structural, mechanical, and electrical drawings and specifications. Duplication of such items as excavation for utilities, temporary services, concrete for the mechanical trades could mean duplication in the bid figures and thus a hidden